CALIFORNIA AGRICULTURAL DIRECTORY 1992

i

Clark Biggs
Editor

Rebecca Rashleigh
Associate Editor

Sherri Freeman
Art Director

Rhonda Asher
Typesetting

Karin Bakotich
Production

Warren Rashleigh
Cover Design

Published by
CALIFORNIA SERVICE AGENCY
1601 Exposition Blvd. FB-10
Sacramento, CA 95815
(916) 924-4360

Milton Levy
Editor Emeritus

Literally thousands of changes and corrections have been made to update the 1992 California Agricultural Directory from its predecessor. In a dynamic industry such as agriculture in such a dynamic state, people and indeed organizations come and go. We have done our best to bring you the latest updated information to make it easier to get around the complex system we call California agriculture.

This year we have added yet another government agency, this time the California Environmental Protection Agency or Cal-EPA. It has assumed some of the pesticide regulation activities of the California Department of Food and Agriculture as well as combining other agencies which may have an effect on agriculture.

As we have advised before, not all organizations that you might think begin with the word "California" actually do, as in "League of...," "Association of...," "Council of...". If you don't find it in the Index, try the Commodity Index which immediately follows it.

We want to thank the many people who have helped us in compiling this newest book, particularly those dedicated professionals at the California Department of Food and Agriculture. We also thank the University of California Cooperative Extension, our fellow staff members at the California Farm Bureau Federation and government agencies in Washington and Oregon.

We need to take a moment this year to commend a special person. Rebecca Rashleigh, known to her myriad friends and acquaintances as Becky, says this is probably her last CAD before retirement. Becky is listed as the associate editor but Becky *is* the California Agricultural Directory. She painstakingly pursues that elusive perfection in all the listings herein with dogged dedication that only a true professional possesses.

If Becky does decide to leave us she will be greatly missed, especially by the editor who works with her daily on this and many other projects.

Clark Biggs
Editor

CALIFORNIA AGRICULTURAL DIRECTORY, 1992
TABLE OF CONTENTS

Page

Introduction..iii
Table of Contents..iv
Index..v-xi
Commodity Index...xii

PART I   California Farm Cooperatives, Agricultural, and Related Organizations.......................1-34
    General..1-6
    Livestock and Dairy...6-12
    Field Crops..12-15
    Fruits and Nuts..15-22
    Vegetables...22-23
    Forest and Forest Products..23
    Floral & Nursery Products...24
    Seeds..24
    Production Services, Financial Services, Farm Labor.....................................24-27
    Water & Resource Conservation...27-34

PART II   Marketing Orders, Commissions and Related State and Federal Programs.................35-38

PART III   Education, Research, Administration, State and Federal Government.................39-40
    Cooperative Extension—University of California (Farm Advisors)...................40-42
    State of California, Department of Food and Agriculture.............................43-44
    County Agricultural Commissioners...44-47
    County Sealers, Weights and Measures..48-50
    Certified Farmers Markets...50-57
    Farm Trails..57-58
    California State Resources Agency...58
    California Environmental Protection Agency (Cal-EPA)..................................59
    U.S. Departments of Agriculture and Interior..60-64
    Federal Information Centers...64

PART IV   Fair Associations..65-68

PART V   California Agricultural Publications...69-72

PART VI   Oregon and Washington Farmer Cooperatives and Farm Organizations...............73-89
    Oregon Farmer Cooperatives / Agricultural Organizations.............................73-80
    Oregon Farm Organizations and Commodity Commissions.............................80-81
    Washington Commodity Commissions..82-83
    Washington Farmer Cooperatives...83-86
    Washington Agricultural Associations...86-89

PART VII   Statistical Section..90-108
    California Farm Income and Production..90-91
    Top 20 Commodities...92
    Comparative Rankings of Major Commodities..93-98
    Leading Counties..99
    Top 20 States, Cash Receipts...100
    Market Value, Farm Real Estate...101
    Market Value Per Acre—Orchards/Vineyards/Groves...............................102-103
    Prices Received—Field Crops/Fruits/Livestock/Livestock Products/Vegetables.....104-105
    Comparison Rainfall—1989-90, 1990-91..106
    Estimated Value of California's Leading Agricultural Exports............................107
    California's Agricultural Export Profile, 1990..108

INDEX

Ag Fresno Farm Equipment Show.............................1
Ag Employers, Inc...26
Agricultural Council of California............................1
Agricultural Education Foundation 1
Agricultural Employers Labor Report 26
Agricultural Leadership Alumni 1
Agricultural Personnel Management
    Association...1
Agricultural Producers 26
Agriservices Foundation 1
Alameda County Fair..65
Alameda County Farm Bureau.................................2
Alfalfa Seed Production Research Board.................36
Alliance for Food & Fiber 1
Alliance of Western Milk Producers........................8
Allied Citrus Exchange...17
Allied Grape Growers...19
Almond Board of California 35
Almond Growers Council 1
Alta Vista Gin...12
Amador County Fair...65
Amador County Farm Bureau 2
AMCOT..12
American Buckskin Registry Association, Inc. 10
American Farmland Trust...1
American Frozen Food Institute................................15
American Mule Association 10
American Sheep Industry Association 11
American Society of Farm Managers and Rural
    Appraisers, California Chapter..............................1
Antelope Valley Fair and Alfalfa Festival....................65
Apple Growers Ice and Cold Storage 16
Apple Hill Growers..16
Apricot Producers of California................................16
Artichoke Advisory Board 36
Associated California Loggers 23
Associated Independent Dairies of America 8
Association of Consulting Foresters..........................23
Atwater Fruit Exchange...15
Avocado Growers Association..................................16
Baird-Neece Packing Corporation 18
Bagdassarian, Richard, Inc......................................18
Baker Brothers..17
Bay Area Air Quality Management District
    Advisory Council 1
Bay Area Marketing Group.......................................1
Bear Creek Winery...19
Bear River Almond Hulling Cooperative, Inc. 21
Beverage Source, Inc., The......................................19
Big Fresno Fair..65
Blue Anchor, California Fruit Exchange 15
Blue Banner Fruit Exchange.....................................17
Blue Banner Company, Inc. 17
Blue Diamond Growers...21
Bonita Packing Company 22
Bovetti Packing...15
Broadview Co-op Gin, Inc. 12
Brown, L.V.W. Estate, Inc...18
Buena Ventura Lemon..26
Bullard Ginning Company...12

Butte County Almond Hull Association 21
Butte County Fair..65
Butte County Farm Bureau.......................................2
Butte County Rice Growers Association....................15
C.R.S. Ginning Company..13
Calaveras County Fair and Jumping
    Frog Jubilee...65
Calaveras County Farm Bureau 2
Calavo Growers of California....................................16
Cal-Bean and Grain Cooperative, Inc. 12
CALCOT, Ltd...12
California Agricultural Aircraft Association 1
California Agricultural Commissioners &
    Sealers Association..1
California Agricultural Foundation 1
California Agricultural Production Consultants
    Association...1
California Agriculture Teachers Association................1
California Almond Growers Exchange........................21
California Ammonia Company 24
California Apricot Advisory Board.............................36
California Aquaculture Association...........................10
California Arizona Citrus League 17
California & Hawaiian Sugar Company (C&H)...........15
California Artichoke and Vegetable Growers
    Corp...22
California Asparagus Commission............................35
California Association of Family Farmers 1
California Association of Nurserymen........................24
California Association of Resource
    Conservation Districts..34
California Association of Wheat Growers 14
California Association of Winegrape Growers.............19
California Avocado Commission 36
California Bean Growers Association........................12
California Beef Cattle Improvement
    Association...7
California Beef Council...38
California Beet Growers Association, Ltd...................15
California Canning Peach Association.......................20
California Cattlemen's Association 7
    Member County Associations...............................7-8
California Celery Research Advisory Board 37
California Certified Organic Farmers.........................1, 2
California Chamber of Commerce Agricultural
    Committee 2
California Cherry Growers & Industry
    Foundation...17
California Cherry Export Association 17
California Christmas Tree Growers 23
California Chrysanthemum Growers
    Association...24
California Citrus Mutual 17
California Citrus Quality Council 17
California Cling Peach Advisory Board 37
California Commission for Food and Wines................2
California Cooperative Creamery 9
California Corn Growers..22
California Cotton Ginners Association.......................12
California Crop Improvement Association..................24
California Dairy Goat Marketing
    Association...10

California Dairy Goat Improvement
   Association (DGHIA)..10
California Creamery Operators Association 8
California Cut Flower Commission............................37
California Dairy Herd Improvement
   Association..9
California Date Administrative Committee..................35
California Desert Grape Administrative
   Committee 35
California Dressage Society 10
California Dried Fruit Export Association...................20
California Egg Commission 37
California Exposition and State Fair 65
California Farm Bureau Federation............................2
California Farm Bureau Federation Political
   Action Committee (FARM PAC®) 4
California Farm Equipment Show &
   International Exposition 4
California Fertilizer Association..................................4
California Fig Advisory Board 37
California Fig Institute 20
California Floral Council 24
California Flower Cooperative 24
California Flower Market 24
California Forestry Association 23
California Foundation for Agriculture in
   The Classroom 2
California Freestone Peach Association.....................20
California Fresh Carrot Advisory Board 37
California Fresh Fruit Growers, Inc...........................15
California Fuyu Growers Association 15
California Grain and Feed Association.......................14
California Granny Smith Association..........................16
California Grape and Tree Fruit League.....................15
California Growers Foundation..................................26
California Holstein Association 9
California Horse Racing Board 10
California Iceberg Lettuce Commission 37
California Institute for Rural Studies...........................4
California Kiwifruit Commission 37
California League of Food Processors.........................4
California Macadamia Society 21
California Manufacturing Milk
   Advisory Board 37
California Mid-State Fair 65
California Mid-Winter Fair 65
California Milk Producers 9
California Milk Advisory Board 37
California Mushroom Growers Cooperative
   Association...22
California-Nevada Hereford Association......................8
California-Nevada Polled Hereford
   Association...8
California North Coast Grape Growers 19
California Olive Association 20
California Olive Committee 35
California Pear Growers 20
California Pecan Growers Association........................21
California Pepper Commission 37
California Pistachio Commission...........................21, 37
California Planting Cotton Seed Distributors 12
California Pork Producers 10

California Potato Research Advisory Board 38
California Poultry Health Board............................11, 38
California Poultry Industry Foundation 11, 38
California Processing Tomato
   Advisory Board 38
California Processor Inc. 5
California Protea Association.....................................24
California Prune Board..38
California Raisin Advisory Board 38
California Redwood Association.................................23
California Rice Industry Association...........................38
California Rice Promotion Board 38
California Rural Crime Prevention Task Force 5
California Seed Association..24
California Seed Council 24
California, State of (See Pages 43-59)
   Department of Food & Agriculture..........................43
      Executive Offices 43
      Division of Administrative Services 43
      Division of Animal Industry 43
      Division of Fairs & Exposition 43
      Division of Inspection Services 43
      Division of Marketing Services 44
      Division of Measurement Standards 44
      Division of Plant Industry 44
      County Agricultural Commissioners 44-47
      State Board Members 48
      County Sealers & Weights and
         Measures 48-50
      Certified Farmers Markets 50-57
      Farm Trail Organizations 57-58
      Division, State Resources Agency 58
California Environmental Protection
   Agency (Cal—EPA)..58-59
California State Beekeepers Association.......................6
California State Florists Association 24
California State Grange 5
California State Horsemen's Association 10
California Strawberry Advisory Board........................38
California Sweet Potato Growers
   Association...22
California Table Grape Commission 35-37
California Thoroughbred Breeders
   Association...10
California Tomato Board 38
California Tomato Growers
   Association, Inc. 22
California Tomato Research Institute, Inc. 22
California Tree Fruit Agreement.................................35
California Veterinary Medical Association 5
California Walnut Commission...................................36
California Weed Conference 5
California Wheat Commission....................................38
California Wild Rice Program.....................................38
California Women for Agriculture.................................5
California Women in Timber 23
California Wool Growers Associations 11
   Branch Wool Growers 11
Calolina Ginning Company 12
Cal-West Seeds..24
Cal-Western Appaloosa Racing Inc. 10
Cal-Wool Marketing Association................................11

Cantaloupe Advisory Board 36
Cantua Co-op Gin 12
Caruthers Co-op Gin, Inc. 12
Castroville Artichoke People 22
Central California Almond Growers
    Association 21
Central California Citrus Exchange 17
Central California Farmers Association, Inc. 26
Central California Lettuce Producers
    Cooperative 22
Central California Tomato Growers
    Cooperative, Inc. 22
Central Coast Agricultural Task Force 5
Central Valley Almond Association, Inc. 21
Central Valley Co-op 12
Central Valley Watermelon Growers
    Association 37
Certified Farmers Markets 50-57
Challenge Dairy Products, Inc. 9
Chico Bean Growers 12
Chico Christmas Fair 65
Chowchilla Madera County Fair 65
Church-Borchard-Murphy 12
Citrus Research Board 37
Cloverdale Citrus Fair 65
Coachella Valley Citrus 18
Coalinga Farmers Co-op Gin, Inc. 12
Coit Ginning Company 12
Colorado River County Fair 65
Colusa County Fair 65
Colusa Holiday Fair and Craft Show 65
Colusa County Farm Bureau 2
Colusa Farm Show 5
Commonwealth Club of California Agriculture
    Study Section 5
Consolidated Milk Producers of Kings County 9
Contra Costa County Fair 65
Contra Costa County Farm Bureau 2
Cooperative Extension Service (See Univ. of
    Calif., Division of) 40-42
Cotton Associates, Inc. 12
Cortez Growers Association, Inc. 22
County Dairy Herd Improvement
    Associations 9
County Farm Bureaus 2, 3, 4
County Line Gin, Inc. 13
Cribari Winery 19
Dairy Council of California 38
Dairy Institute of California 9
Dairymen's Cooperative Creamery Association 9
Dairymen's Feed and Supply Cooperative 24
Danish Creamery Association 9
Del Norte County Farm Bureau 2
Delano Growers Grape Products 19
Del Norte County Fair 65
Desert Empire Fair 65
Diamond Walnut Growers, Inc. 16, 22
Dichondra Council 24
Diversified Producers Cooperative
    Association 22
Dixon May Fair & Christmas Faire 65
Dos Palos Co-op 13

Dried Fruit Association of California 20
Dry Bean Advisory Board 36
Eagle Field Ginning Co. 13
Eastcardale Co-op Gin, Inc. 13
Eastern Sierra Tri County Fair 65
East-Side Winery 19
Elbow Enterprises, Inc. 13
El Dorado County Fair 65
El Dorado County Farm Bureau 2
El Dorado Ranch Marketing Guide 5
Exeter Citrus Association 18
F & P Growers Association 26
Farm Employers Labor Service 26
Farmers Fair of Riverside County 65
Farm Trails Organizations 57-58
Farmers Cold Storage & Freezers, Inc. 16
Farmers Co-op Gin, Inc. 13
Farmers Rice Cooperative 15
Federal Land Bank Associations:
Production Credit Associations:
    Bakersfield, Central Coast, Central Valley,
    Colusa-Glenn, El Centro-Imperial-Yuma,
    Fresno-Madera, Sierra Nevada, Kingsburg,
    North Coast, Northern California, Pacific Coast,
    Sacramento Valley, Sierra Bay, Southern California,
    Visalia, Yosemite 25-26
Fillmore-Piru Citrus Association 17
Fillmore-Piru Citrus Exchange 17
Foothill Properties 16
Forest Land Owners of California 23
Fresh Garlic Association 5
Fresh Produce Council 22
Fresno Chamber of Commerce Agribusiness
    Council 5
Fresno Cooperative Raisin Growers 21
Fresno County Farm Bureau 2
Frozen Vegetable Council 22
Fruit Growers Laboratory, Inc. 16
Fruit Growers Supply Company 25
Future Farmers of America Foundation 5
Gibson Wine Company 19
Gillette Citrus Co. 17
Glenn County Fair 65
Glenn County Farm Bureau 2
Glenn Milk Producers Association 9
Gold Country Fair 66
Gold Ribbon Potato Company 15
Golden State Co-op Gins 13
Golden State Citrus Packers 18
Golden State Walnut Growers Association 22
Golden Valley Citrus, Inc. 17
Grand National Foundation 6
Grand National Livestock Exposition
    Horse Show & Rodeo 65
Grand View Heights Citrus Association 18
Grape Improvement Association 19
Great Snail Festival 66
Great Western Livestock & Expo 65
Greenville Warehouse 12
Growers Farm Labor Association 26
Growers Harvesting Committee 26
Grower-Shipper Vegetable Association of
    Central California 22, 26

Grower-Shipper Vegetable Association of
  Santa Barbara & San Luis
  Obispo Counties..22, 26
Growers Westmorland Gin 13
Guild Wineries and Distilleries..................................19
H & H Ginning...13
H & R Citrus 17
Half Moon Bay Growers Association.........................22
Harding and Leggett, Inc. 18
Humboldt County Fair...66
Humboldt County Farm Bureau 3
Huron Ginning Company 13
Iceberg Lettuce Research Advisory Board 37
Imperial County Farm Bureau 3
Imperial Grain Growers, Inc.......................................14
Imperial Valley Vegetable Growers
  Association...23
Independent Growers Association, Inc.......................26
Index Fresh of California...16
Inter-Mountain Fair of Shasta County 66
International Agri-Center, Inc..5
International Arabian Horse Association.....................10
International Sprout Growers Association 23
Inyo/Mono County Farm Bureau 3
Island Co-op Gin, Inc...13
Ivanhoe Citrus Association 17
Jackson/Mitchell, Inc..10
Jojoba Southwest, Inc..12
Josh's Jamboree...66
Junior Grand National Livestock
  Exposition Horse Show & Rodeo.............................66
Kaweah Citrus Association #1 17
Kaweah Citrus Association #2 17
Kelseyville Packing Company.....................................20
Kerman Co-op Gin & Warehouse, Inc. 13
Kern County Fair/Kern County Country
  Horse Fair...66
Kern County Farm Bureau 3
Kern County Hay Growers Association.......................15
Kern Delta-Weedpatch Cotton Ginning Co. 13
Kern Lake Co-op Gin...13
Kings County Farm Bureau 3
Kings District Fair...66
Kiwifruit Administrative Committee 35
Kiwifruit Growers of California....................................20
Klink Citrus Association..18
Lake County Fair...66
Lake County Farm Bureau 3
Lake County Grape Growers.......................................19
Landmark Produce Sales..16
Lassen County Fair 66
Lassen County Farm Bureau..3
Laton Co-op Gin, Inc. 13
Lawson Packing 17
Lemon Administrative Committee 35
Limoneira Company 18
Lindsay Fruit Association 17
Lindsay International Inc. 20
Lindsay Olive Growers..20
Livingston Farmers Association 16, 23
Lodi District Grape Growers Association 19
Lodi District Vintners Association...............................19

Lodi Grape Festival & National
  Wine Show 66
Loomis Fruit Growers Association 16
Los Angeles Area Chamber of Commerce
  Natural Resources and Environment
  Council...5
Los Angeles County Fair...66
Los Angeles County Farm Bureau................................3
Los Padres Growers Foundation.................................26
Madera District Chamber of Commerce/
  Agri-Business Committee 5
Madera Co-op Gin, Inc...13
Madera District Fair...66
Madera County Farm Bureau 3
Magnolia Citrus Association 18
Marin County Fair 66
Marin County Farm Bureau 3
Marin Horse Council..10
Mariposa County Fair..66
Mariposa County Farm Bureau 3
Marlin Packing Company...18
Mayflower Fruit Association..16
McFarland Co-op Gin, Inc. 13
McKinney Packing, Inc..17
Melon Research Board 37
Mendocino County Fair & Apple Show 66
Mendocino County Farm Bureau..................................3
Mendocino County Farm Supply Company................25
Mendocino County Vintners Association 19
Mendocino Vineyards Winery 19
Merced County Fair...66
Merced County Farm Bureau..3
Merced County Spring Fair-Los Banos.......................66
Mesa Citrus Growers..17
Mid-California Citrus Exchange 18
Mid Valley Cotton Growers, Inc. 13
Milk Producers Council 10
Millwood Packing..17
Minturn Cooperative Gin, Inc./
  Minturn Red Top..13
Minturn Huller Cooperative, Inc..................................21
Mission Citrus 18
Modern Ginning Company...13
Modesto Chamber of Commerce Agribusiness
  Division..5
Modoc County Farm Bureau...3
Modoc District Fair..66
Monterey Bay Flowers Growers 24
Monterey County Fair..66
Monterey County Farm Bureau 3
Monterey County Grape Growers Association............19
Monterey Greenhouse Company.................................24
Monterey National Horse Show 66
Monterey Wine Country Associates 19
Mother Lode Fair 66
Mt. Konocti Growers, Inc. 20, 22
Mt. Whitney Ginning Co. 13
NAMA Cal (National Agri-Marketing
  Association)..5
NAMA West (National Agri-Marketing
  Association)..5
Napa County Fair...66

Napa County Farm Bureau 3
Napa County Farm Supply 25
Napa Town & Country Fair &
   Spring Fair...67
Napa Valley Cooperative Winery 19
Napa Valley Grape Growers....................................19
Napa Valley Vintners Association 20
National Cattlemen's Association 6
National Farmers Organization, Regional
   Marketing Office..5
National Orange Packing Company 18
National Orange Show 67
Naturipe Berry Growers...17
Nevada County Fair 67
Nevada County Farm Bureau....................................3
Newell Grain Growers Association 14
Newell Potato Cooperative, Inc...............................15
Nisei Farmers League..26
Nor-Cal NAMA (National Agri-Marketing
   Association...5
North Coast Livestock Protective Association 8
North State Hulling Cooperative, Inc.......................21
Northern Merced Hulling Association 21
Nulaid Foods, Inc...11
Nursery Growers Association of California.................24
Oberti Olives 20
Ojai-Tapo Citrus Association 18
Olive Growers Council 20
Orange Administrative Committee............................35
Orange County Fair 67
Orange County Farm Bureau.....................................3
Orange County Fruit Exchange................................18
Orange Cove-Sanger Citrus Association 18
Orange Heights Orange Association 18
Oregon-California Potato Marketing
   Committee 36
Oregon, State of (See pages 73-81)
   Farmer Cooperatives/Organizations/
   Commissions
Oxnard Berry Farm 17
Oxnard Lemon Company 17
Oxnard Pest Control Association/
   Beneficial Insects..5
Pacific Coast Producers 16
Pacific Coast Quarter Horse Association..................10
Pacific Egg & Poultry Association 11
Pacific Racing Association 10
Paloma Citrus Association..18
Panoche Ginning Co., Inc. 13
PCA Feed & Supply, Inc. 11
Peanut Administrative Committee 36
Pear Program Committee...38
People's Organization for Land
   Preservation (P.O.L.P.)...5
Pesticide Applicators Professional
   Association (PAPA)...6
Pistachio Producers of California 38
Placer County Fair 67
Placer County Farm Bureau.......................................3
Placer Farm Supply...25
Placerville Fruit Growers Association........................16
Planters Ginning Co. / Weist Gin 13
Plumas County Fair..67

Plumas-Sierra County Farm Bureau 3
Porterville Citrus Association, The............................18
Processing Strawberry Advisory Board 38
Producers Livestock Marketing Associations...............6
Production Credit Associations:
Federal Land Bank Associations:
   Bakersfield, Central Coast, Central Valley
   Colusa-Glenn, El Centro-Imperial-Yuma
   Fresno-Madera, Sierra Nevada,
   Kingsburg, North Coast, Northern California,
   Pacific Coast, Sacramento Valley
   Sierra Bay, Southern California,
   Visalia, Yosemite..25, 26
Production Farm Management, Inc. 17
Prune Bargaining Association 21
Prune Marketing Committee 36
Raisin Administrative Committee..............................36
Raisin Bargaining Association, Inc...........................21
Raisin City Co-op Gin, Inc. 14
Ranchers Cotton Oil 14
Red Bluff Bull & Gelding Sale...................................8
Red Top Rice Growers 15
Redlands Foothill Groves 16, 18
Redwood Acres Fair 67
Redwood Empire Fair/ Spring Fair...........................67
Redwood Region Conservation Council 23
Redwood Region Logging Conference 23
Rice Growers Association of California 15
Rice Research Board 38
Richland Co-op Gin, Inc. 14
Ridge Ginning Co. 14
Ripley Ginning Corp./ Ripley
   Ginning L/S 14
Riverside-Arlington Heights Fruit Exchange 18
Riverside County Farm Bureau 3
Riverside County National Date
   Festival..67
River Valley Marketing 23
Royal Citrus Company 18
Royal Citrus Exchange...18
Royal Valley Fruit Growers Association.....................16
SRI International...6
Sacramento County Fair—Cal Expo 67
Sacramento County Farm Bureau 3
Sacramento Valley Landowners Association 27
Salida Hulling Association 21
Salinas Lettuce Farmers Co-op 23
Salinas Valley Fair 67
San Antonio Orchard Company 16
San Benito County Fair...67
San Benito County Saddle Horse
   Show and Rodeo...67
San Benito County Farm Bureau 3
San Bernardino County Fair 67
San Bernardino County Farm Bureau.........................3
San Bernardino Valley Egg Producers
   Association...11
San Diego County Farm Bureau 4
San Diego County Flower Growers
   Association...24
San Fernando Valley Fair 67
San Francisco Fair & Exposition 67
San Francisco Flower Growers Association 24

San Joaquin County Fair 67
San Joaquin County Farm Bureau...........................4
San Joaquin Farm Production Association 26
San Joaquin Livestock Marketing, Inc. 10
San Joaquin Valley Cherry Shippers.........................17
San Joaquin Valley Dairymen.....................................10
San Joaquin Valley Hay Growers Association 15
San Joaquin Valley NAMA (National
    Agri-Marketing Association....................................6
San Luis Obispo County Farm Bureau......................4
San Luis Obispo County Farm Bureau Grain
    Improvement Association 14
San Luis Obispo County Farm Supply
    Company 25
San Mateo County Fair..67
San Mateo County Farm Bureau 4
San Mateo County Farm Supply Company................25
Santa Barbara County Fair &
    Horse Show...67
Santa Barbara Exposition &
    Fair & Flower Show...67
Santa Barbara County Farm Bureau............................4
Santa Barbara National Amateur
    Horse Show...67
Santa Barbara National Horse Show 67
Santa Clara County Fair 67
Santa Clara County Farm Bureau 4
Santa Clara County Harvest Fair................................67
Santa Clara County Holiday Fair 67
Santa Clara Valley Winegrowers.................................20
Santa Cruz County Farm Bureau 4
Santa Cruz Mountain Vintners 20
Santa Paula Orange Association 18
Saticoy Fruit Exchange 18
Saticoy Lemon Association 18
Save-the-Redwoods League.......................................23
Scotts Valley Fruit Exchange 20
Sebastopol Apple Growers United 16
Semi-Tropic Co-op...14
Sequoia Growers Foundation.....................................26
Sequoia Walnut Growers Association 22
Shafter-Wasco Ginning Co. 14
Shasta County Farm Bureau 4
Shasta District Fair 68
Sierra Citrus Association 17
Sierra Vista Packing Co., Inc......................................17
Silver Dollar Fair 68
Sioux Honey Association...6
Siskiyou County Farm Bureau 4
Siskiyou Golden Fair 68
Solano County Fair...68
Solano County Farm Bureau 4
Sonoma County Fair 68
Sonoma County Farm Bureau 4
Sonoma County Wineries Association 20
Sonoma-Marin Fair 68
South Bay Farmers Cooperative Association 23
Southland Farmers' Market Association 6
South Valley Gin, Inc. 14
Southern Arizona Citrus Exchange............................18
Southern California Exposition/
    Del Mar 68
Southern California Flower Growers, Inc....................24

Southern California Growers Foundation 26
Southwest Marketing Corporation 14
Squab Producers of California....................................11
Stanislaus County Fair..68
Stanislaus County Farm Bureau 4
Stanislaus Farm Supply Company.............................25
Stark Packing Corporation 17
Steering Committee for Sustainable
    Agriculture (SCSA) 6
Stockton Ag Expo 6
Stockton District Kidney Bean Growers, Inc. 12
Stratford Growers...14
Strathmore Cooperative Association 18
Strathmore Packing House Company 18
Suisun Valley Fruit Growers Association 16
Sun Country Fair 68
Sun-Diamond Growers of California 16, 21, 22
Sun-Maid Growers of California 21
Sunkist Growers Inc. 17
    Growers/Members 17-19
Sunland Packing House Company..............................18
Sun Pacific Exchange 18
Sun Pacific Shippers 18
Sunshine Foods 11
Sunsweet Growers, Inc. 21
Sutter Basin Growers Cooperative.............................15
Sweet Potato Council of California 23
Tehama County Farm Bureau 4
Tehama County Farm Supply Company......................25
Tokay Marketing Agreement 35
Tri Citrus Association..19
Tri-City Growers, Inc...14
Tri-County Citrus Association 18
Tri Valley Growers 6
Tri Valley Growers—Container Division 25
Trinity County Fair 68
Trinity County Farm Bureau 4
Tulare County Fair...68
Tulare County Farm Bureau 4
Tulare County Fruit Exchange 18
Tulare County Lemon Association 18
Tulare-Kern Citrus Exchange 18
Tulelake-Butte Valley Fair 68
Tulelake Growers Association 23
Tule River Cooperative Dryer, Inc. 21
Tule River Cooperative..14
Tuolumne County Farm Bureau 4
United Agribusiness League 6
University of California Division of
    Agriculture 39
    Agricultural Field Stations 39-40
    Cooperative Extension Service
        & Small Farm Center
    (Farm Home & Youth Advisors) 40-42
U.S. Department of Agriculture, (See pages 60-64)
    Agricultural Research/Laboratories & Field
        Stations 60, 61
    Agriculture Stabilization & Conservation
        Service 61-63
    Farmers Home Administration 63
        District Offices..63
        County Offices..63, 64
        Food & Nutrition 64
        Forest Service...64

U.S. Department of Interior 64
    Bureau of Land Management 64
    Bureau of Reclamation 64
U.S. Federal Information Centers 64
Valley Fig Growers 21
Valley Growers and Packers.....................23
Vegetable Bargaining Association
    of California 27
Ventura County Citrus Growers Committee 27
Ventura County Agricultural Association......................6
Ventura County Citrus Exchange 18
Ventura County Fair 68
Ventura County Farm Bureau 4
Ventura County Fruit Growers, Inc. 18
Ventura County Fruit Exchange.................18
Ventura Pacific Company 18
Villa Park Citrus Exchange 18
Villa Park Orchards Association, Inc., The.................18
Visalia Citrus Packers 19
Visalia Co-op Cotton Gin, Inc. 14
Visalia Fruit Exchange...............................18
Vitagold Brands Cooperative Association..................11
Walnut Marketing Board 36
Washington, State of (See pages 81-89)
    Farmers Cooperatives/Organizations/
    Commissions
Water & Water Related Organizations
    (See pages 27-34)
    Association of California Water
      Agencies 27
    California Central Valley Flood Control
      Association 27
    California Farm Water Coalition..............27
    California Groundwater Association.........27
    California Mutual Water Companies
      Association 27
    California Water Resources Association 27
    Colorado River Association.....................27
    Sacramento Valley Landowners
      Association 27
    State Water Contractors..........................27
    Water Association of Kern County 27
    Water Education Foundation 27
    WateRuse Association of
      California 27
    Water Agencies Active in
      Irrigation 27-34
    Resource Conservation Districts 34
West Coast Reining Horse Association 10
West Coast United Egg Producers 11
West Stanislaus Growers Association 12
West Valley Cotton Growers, Inc...............14
Western Agricultural Chemicals Association................6
Western Brahman Breeders Association 6
Western Cotton Growers Association 14
Western Fairs Association 6
Western Farm Credit Bank 25
Western Grain Marketing, Inc. 15
Western Growers Association.................6, 23
Western Pistachio Association...................22
Western Range Association 12
Western Society of Weed Science 6
Western States Meat Association...............6

Western United Dairymen 10
Westhaven Cotton Company 14
Westlake Farms, Inc. 14
Westside Farmers Coop Gin, Inc. 14
Westside Hulling Association 21
Wheeler Farms 14
Wine Institute 20
Winter Pear Control Committee 36
Woodbridge Vineyard Association 20
Woodland Stallion Station.........................10
Yolo County Fair 68
Yolo County Farm Bureau 4
Yorba Orange Growers Association 18
Yuba-Sutter County Farm Bureau...............4
Yuba Sutter Fair 68
Yuma Mesa Fruit Growers Association 18

COMMODITY INDEX

Alfalfa 36
Almonds 21, 35
Apples 16
Apricots 16, 36
Aquaculture...10
Artichokes..22, 36
Asparagus..35
Avocados 16, 36
Beans 12, 36
Bees 6
Berries...16
Cantaloupes 37
Carrots 37
Cattle 6-7, 38
Celery 37
Cherries 17
Citrus...17-19, 35, 37
Corn 22
Cotton & Cotton Gins.................................12-14
Dairy 6-10, 37, 38
Dates 35
Dried Fruits 20, 21
Eggs 11, 37
Figs 20, 21, 37
Fish 10
Flowers, Nursery Products.............................24
Forest & Forest Products 23
Fowl 11, 38
Fruits..15, 21
Goats..10
Grain 14, 15, 38
Grapes—Wine...........................19-20, 35, 37
Hay..15
Hogs 10
Honey...6
Horses...10
Jojoba 12
Kiwi 20, 35, 37
Lemons (See Citrus)............................17, 18, 35
Lettuce..22, 23, 37
Macadamias..21
Melons...37
Milk..37
Mushrooms 22
Nectarines..35
Nuts 21, 22, 36-38
Olives...20, 35
Oranges (See Citrus) 18, 35
Peaches 20, 35, 37
Pears 20, 35, 36, 38
Peanuts 36
Pecans 21
Peppers...37
Pistachios 21, 22, 37, 38

Plums 35
Poultry 11, 38
Potatoes 15, 36, 38
Prunes...20, 36, 38
Raisins..36, 38
Rice 15, 38
Seeds 24
Sheep..11
Sprouts 23
Strawberries 38
Sugar...15
Sweet Potatoes 22-23
Timber 23
Tomatoes...22, 38
Vegetables 22-23
Walnuts 22, 36
Wheat..38
Wine 19, 20

PART I

Farm Cooperatives, Related Agricultural Organizations, Commodity Groups, Production Services, Water and Resource Agencies

GENERAL

Ag Fresno Farm Equipment Show
1121 Chance Avenue, Fresno 93702
Sid Cox, Show Manager
209-255-0764

Agricultural Council of California
1225 H Street, Sacramento 95814
P.O. Box 1712, Sacramento 95812-1712
Leland H. Ruth, President
916-443-4887   FAX 916-443-0601

Agricultural Education Foundation
P.O. Box 60, Templeton 93465
Tim LaSalle, President
805-434-2680   FAX 805-434-3317

Agricultural Leadership Alumni
P.O. Box 162, Visalia 93279
Adin Hester, Executive Director
209-625-2851   FAX 209-625-4847

Agricultural Personnel Management Association
P.O. 9697, Bakersfield 93309
805-837-1778

Agriservices Foundation
648 West Sierra, Clovis 93612
Dr. M.E. Ensminger, President
209-299-2263

Alliance for Food and Fiber
1047 Gayley Ave., 2nd Floor, Los Angeles 90024
Wade Whitfield, Chairman
213-208-6152   FAX 408-824-2644

Almond Growers Council
P.O. Box 577, McFarland 93250
Brad Munson, President
805-792-2101

American Farmland Trust
1949 Fifth Street, Ste. 101, Davis 95616
Gregory L. Carnill, Director
916-753-1073   FAX (916) 753-1120

American Society of Farm Managers and Rural Appraisers—California Chapter
213 N. Encina, Visalia 93291
Shirley Kirkpatrick, Secretary
209-732-3422   FAX 209-732-1927

Bay Area Air Quality Management District, Advisory Council
939 Ellis Street, San Francisco 94109
Milton Feldstein, Control Officer, Air Pollution
415-771-6000   FAX 415-928-8560

Bay Area Marketing Group
8 La Madronal, Orinda 94563
Richard Strong, Field Representative
510-254-7198

California Agricultural Aircraft Association
2150 River Plaza Drive, Ste. 315
Sacramento 95833-3880
Rob Olson, Executive Director
916-641-1171   FAX 916-924-1554

California Agricultural Commissioners and Sealers Association
3400 La Madera Ave., El Monte 91732
E. Leon Spaugy, Director
818-575-5451   FAX 818-350-7077

California Agricultural Foundation
16040 Amar Rd., City of Industry 91744
Carol Spoelstra-Pepper, Executive Director
818-330-9496

California Agricultural Production Consultants Association
100 Valley View Drive, Petaluma 94952
Stan Strew, Executive Director
707-795-0311   FAX 707-795-8099

California Agricultural Teachers Association
1100 "N" St., Suite 1D, Sacramento 95814
Ken Harris, Executive Director
916-443-2282

California Association of Family Farmers
433 Russell Blvd., Davis 95616
P.O. Box 363, Davis 95617
Tom Haller, Executive Secretary
916-756-7420

California Certified Organic Farmers
P.O. Box 8136, Santa Cruz 95061-8136
Bill Brammer, State President
408-423-2263

Big Valley Chapter
6901 Hultberg Road, Hilmar 95324
209-667-7494

1

Central Coast Chapter
P.O. Box 1413, Freedom 95019
408-728-2022

Desert Valleys
P.O. Box 908, Indio 92202
619-345-6171

Fresno-Tulare Chapter
5587 E. National, Fresno 93727
209-291-0963

Kern Chapter
Rt. 2, Box 291, Delano 93215
805-725-1046

Lake County Chapter
P.O. Box 1243, Kelseyville 95451

Mendocino Chapter
18501 Greenwood Road, Philo 95466
707-895-2333

North Coast Chapter
P.O. Box 2406, Sebastopol 95473-2406
707-874-1357

North Valley Chapter
5034 Larkin Road, Oroville 95965
916-589-0695

Pacific Southwest Chapter
32929 Lilac Road, Valley Center 92082
619-728-9664

San Luis Obispo Chapter
6080 Parkhill Road, Santa Margarita 93453
805-438-4276

Sierra Gold Chapter
7740 Fairplay Rd., Somerset 95684
209-245-3248

Siskiyou-Humboldt
13611 Meamber Creek Road, Fort Jones 96032
916-468-5297

South Coast Chapter
P.O. Box 40144, Santa Barbara 93140
805-687-7109

Yolo Chapter
Star Route Box 3, Capay 95679
916-796-4111

**California Chamber of Commerce
Agricultural Committee**
1201 K St., 12th Floor-P.O. Box 1736
Sacramento 95812-1736
Valerie Nera, Director
916-444-6670   FAX 916-444-6685

California Commission for Food and Wines
P.O. Box 4044, Los Angeles 90051
Stan Jones, Executive Director
818-703-6177

California Farm Bureau Federation
1601 Exposition Blvd., Sacramento 95815
Bob L. Vice, President
916-924-4075   FAX 916-923-5318

**California Foundation For Agriculture
In The Classroom**
1601 Exposition Blvd., Sacramento 95815
Mark Linder, Executive Director
916-924-4380   FAX 916-923-5318

County Farm Bureaus:

Alameda County Farm Bureau
638 Enos Way, Livermore 94550
Diane Andrade, Manager
510-449-1677

Amador County Farm Bureau
34 Summit Street, Suite C, Jackson 95642
Jean Scalon, Manager
209-223-0951

Butte County Farm Bureau
2580 Feather River Blvd., Oroville 95965
Margery L. Taylor, Executive Director
916-533-1473   FAX 916-533-7412

Calaveras County Farm Bureau
571 Stanislaus St., Suite J
P.O. Box 490, Angels Camp 95222
Tina Torres, Manager/Secretary
209-736-4666

Colusa County Farm Bureau
595 7th Street, P.O. Box 459
Williams 95987
Robert Herkert, Executive Manager
916-473-2505   FAX 916-473-5933

Contra Costa County Farm Bureau
5554 Clayton Road, Concord 94521
Mrs. Susan Spannagel, Executive Secretary
510-672-5115   FAX 510-672-8382

Del Norte County Farm Bureau
111 Rowdy Creek Road
P.O. Box 789, Smith River 95567
Marcie V. Houser, Secretary/Treasurer
707-487-8095

El Dorado County Farm Bureau
2460 Headington Road, Placerville 95667
Ms. Michel Miller, Manager
916-622-7773

Fresno County Farm Bureau
1274 West Hedges, Fresno 93728
C.W. "Bill" Allison, Manager
209-237-0263   FAX 209-237-3396

Glenn County Farm Bureau
501 Walker Street, Orland 95963
Cindy Cushman, Manager
916-865-9636   FAX 916-865-3324

Humboldt County Farm Bureau
P.O. Box 308, Fields Landing 95537
5601 S. Broadway, Eureka 95501
Katherine Queen, Executive Director
707-443-4844   FAX 707-443-0611

Imperial County Farm Bureau
1000 Broadway, El Centro 92243
Wes Bisgaard, Manager
619-352-3831   FAX 619-352-0232

Inyo/Mono County Farm Bureau
218 S. Main, Ste. D1, Bishop 93514
Ms. Andy Rossi, Secretary
619-873-7398

Kern County Farm Bureau
2724 "L" Street, P.O. Box 2425,
Bakersfield 93303
Loren Hodge, Secretary/Manager
805-323-7897   FAX 805-323-4138

Kings County Farm Bureau
870 W. Greenfield Avenue, Hanford 93230
Kelly Maytubby, Executive Director
209-584-3557   FAX 209-584-1614

Lake County Farm Bureau
65 Soda Bay Road, Lakeport 95453
Raymond Mostin, Manager
707-263-0911

Lassen County Farm Bureau
626 Main St., Susanville 96130
Michelle Upton, Secretary
916-257-7242

Los Angeles County Farm Bureau
1006 West Lancaster Blvd., Lancaster 93534
Patty Zellers, Executive/Secretary
805-948-6571

Madera County Farm Bureau
13314 Road 26, Madera 93637
Betty Crawford, Secretary/Manager
209-674-8871

Marin County Farm Bureau
P.O. Box 219, 520 Mesa Road
Point Reyes Station 94956
Phyllis Hartley, Executive Director
415-663-1231

Mariposa County Farm Bureau
5131 Highway 140,
P.O. Box 1297, Mariposa 95338
Kinzetta Trimble, Secretary/Manager
209-966-3848

Mendocino County Farm Bureau
303-C Talmadge Road, Ukiah 95482
Carre Brown, Executive Administrator
707-462-6664   FAX 707-462-6681

Merced County Farm Bureau
646 S. Highway 59, Merced 95340
P.O. Box 1232, Merced 95341
Mike Wade, Manager
209-723-3001   FAX 209-722-3814

Modoc County Farm Bureau
105 West 2nd Street, P.O. Box 1692
Alturas 96101
Pat Enz, Secretary
916-233-3276   FAX 916-233-3276

Monterey County Farm Bureau
512 Pajaro St., Salinas 93901
William H. Barker, Executive Director
408-422-9063   FAX 408-422-9065

Napa County Farm Bureau
4075 Solano Avenue, Napa 94558
Mary Handel, Executive Director
707-224-5403   FAX 707-224-7836

Nevada County Farm Bureau
P.O. Box 27, Grass Valley 95945
John Taylor, Secretary/Manager
916-272-1007

Orange County Farm Bureau
2512 Chambers Rd., Ste. 203, Tustin 92680
Nanci Jimenez, Manager
714-573-0374   FAX 714-573-0376

Placer County Farm Bureau
10120 Ophir Road, P.O. Box 317
Newcastle 95658
Mrs. Lillian Kennedy, Executive Secretary
916-663-2929

Plumas-Sierra County Farm Bureau
P.O. Box 35, Loyalton 96118
Mrs. Helen Roberti, Secretary/Treasurer
916-993-4550

Riverside County Farm Bureau
21160 Box Springs Road, Suite 102,
Moreno Valley 92557
Robert Perkins, Executive Manager
714-684-6732   FAX 714-782-0621

Sacramento County Farm Bureau
8467 Florin Road, Sacramento 95828
J R Nelson, Executive Manager
916-383-2841   FAX 916-383-2842

San Benito County Farm Bureau
341 Tres Pinos Road, Ste. 202A, Hollister 95023
Mildred Freeborn, Executive Director
408-637-7643

San Bernardino County Farm Bureau
210 South Riverside Avenue, Rialto 92376
Dona Throop, Manager
714-875-5945

San Diego County Farm Bureau
1670 East Valley Parkway, Escondido 92027
Dave Owen, Executive Director
619-745-3023   FAX 619-489-6348

San Joaquin County Farm Bureau
3290 North Ad Art Way, Stockton 95205
P.O. Box 8444, Stockton 95208
Robert Cabral, Executive Manager
209-931-4931   FAX 209-931-1433

San Luis Obispo County Farm Bureau
651 Tank Farm Road, San Luis Obispo 93401
Marilyn Britton, Executive Manager
805-543-3654   FAX 805-543-3697

San Mateo County Farm Bureau
765 Main Street, Half Moon Bay 94019
Betty Stone, Executive Manager
415-726-4485   FAX 415-726-4495

Santa Barbara County Farm Bureau
180 Industrial Way, P.O. Box 1846 Buellton 93427
Richard Morgantini, Secretary/Manager
805-688-7479   FAX 805-688-2248

Santa Clara County Farm Bureau
1368 North 4th Street, San Jose 95112
Suzanne Ketcherside, Executive Director
408-453-0100   FAX 408-453-0102

Santa Cruz County Farm Bureau
141 Monte Vista Ave., Watsonville 95076
Jess Brown, Executive Director
408-724-1356   FAX 408-724-5821

Shasta County Farm Bureau
3605 Bechelli Lane, Redding 96001
Shawna DeSilva, Secretary/Manager
916-223-2358

Siskiyou County Farm Bureau
809 South 4th Street, Yreka 96097
Joan Smith, Executive Director
916-842-2364   FAX 916-842-5041

Solano County Farm Bureau
2210 Boynton Ave, Ste. E, Fairfield 94533
Mary Ann Diehl, Executive Secretary
707-425-8044

Sonoma County Farm Bureau
970 Piner Road, Santa Rosa 95403
P.O. Box 6674, Santa Rosa 95406
Judy Van Winkle, Executive Director
707-544-5575   FAX 707-542-8130

Stanislaus County Farm Bureau
1201 L Street, Modesto 95354
P.O. Box 3070, Modesto 95353
Jan Ennenga, Executive Manager
209-522-7278   FAX 209-521-9938

Tehama County Farm Bureau
1130 Metzger Rd., Red Bluff 96080
Claudia Pickard, Executive Secretary
916-527-7882   FAX 916-527-8312

Trinity County Farm Bureau
P.O. Box 1216, Hayfork 96041
Carole Lucan, Secretary
916-628-5030

Tulare County Farm Bureau
737 North Ben Maddox Way, P.O. Box 748,
Visalia 93279
Laurena Johnson, Executive Director
209-732-8301   FAX 209-732-7029

Tuolumne County Farm Bureau
18971 Hess Ave., Suite C, Sonora 95370
Cheryl Thompson, Secretary
209-532-5102

Ventura County Farm Bureau
5156 McGrath Street, Ventura 93003
P.O. Box 3160, Ventura 93006
Rex Laird, Executive Director
805-656-3552   FAX 805-642-2303

Yolo County Farm Bureau
69 West Kentucky Avenue, P.O. Box 1556
Woodland 95695
Elaine Timothy, Secretary/Manager
916-662-6316

Yuba-Sutter County Farm Bureau
475 Palora Avenue, Yuba City 95991
Doris Joaquin, Executive Secretary
916-673-6550   FAX 916-671-5836

California Farm Bureau Federation Political Action Committee (FARM PAC®)
1601 Exposition Blvd., Sacramento 95815
John Peace, Director
916-924-4379   FAX 916-923-5318

California Farm Equipment Show & International Exposition
P.O. Box 1475, Tulare 93275
Gary D. Schulz, General Manager
209-688-1751   FAX 209-686-5065

California Fertilizer Association
1700 "I" Street, Ste. 130, Sacramento 95814
Steven R. Beckley, Executive Vice President
916-441-1584   FAX 916-441-2569

California Institute for Rural Studies
P.O. Box 2143, Davis 95617
Don Villarejo, Director
916-756-6555

California League of Food Processors
1112 "I" Street, Ste. 100, Sacramento 95814
Lawrence Taber, President
916-444-9260   FAX 916-444-2746

California Processor Inc.
425 Military East, Ste. J,
Benicia 94510
Bernard Eilerts, President
707-747-6055   FAX 707-747-6059

California Rural Crime Prevention Task Force
Attorney General's Office,
Crime Prevention Center
P.O. Box 161775, Sacramento 95816
Raymond Konrad, Program Supervisor
916-324-7863   FAX 916-324-5205

California State Grange
2101 Stockton Blvd., Sacramento 95817
William R. Booth, Master
916-454-5805

California Veterinary Medical Association
5231 Madison Ave., Sacramento 95841
Dick Schumacher, DVN, Executive Director
916-344-4985

California Weed Conference
P.O. Box 609, Fremont 94537-0609
Wanda Graves, Business Manager/Treasurer
510-790-1252

California Women for Agriculture
81 Castroville Rd., Salinas 93907
Sharon Lanini, President
408-757-2400   FAX 408-757-9868

Central Coast Agricultural Task Force
1000 S. Main St., Ste.686, Salinas 93901
Thelma Moses, Legislative Consultant
408-424-6221

Colusa Farm Show
P.O. Box 240, Colusa 95932
Raymond R. Gibbs, Secretary/Manager
916-458-2661

Commonwealth Club of California, Agriculture Study Section
595 Market Street, San Francisco 94105
Jerome B. Siebert, Section Chairman
415-597-6700   FAX 415-597-6729

El Dorado Ranch Marketing Guide
c/o El Dorado County Chamber of Commerce
542 Main Street, Placerville 95667
916-621-5885 or 800-457-6279

Fresh Garlic Association
P.O. Box 2410, Sausalito 94966-2410
Frank Pitts, President
415-383-5057

Fresno Chamber of Commerce
Agribusiness Council
P.O. Box 1469, Fresno 93716
Agribusiness Director
209-233-4651   FAX 209-233-6631

Future Farmers of America Foundation
P.O. Box 1283, Sacramento 95812-1283
Ken Harris, Executive Director
916-448-0766

International Agri-Center, Inc.
4450 So. Laspina, 93274
P.O. Box 1475, Tulare 93275
Gary Schulz, Show Director
209-688-1751   FAX 209-686-5065

Los Angeles Area Chamber of Commerce
Natural Resources & Environment Council
404 S. Bixel Street, Los Angeles 90017
P.O. Box 3696, Los Angeles 90051
Larry Bacharach, Program Director
213-629-0668

Madera District Chamber of Commerce
Agribusiness Committee
131 W. Yosemite Ave., Madera 93637
209-673-3563   FAX 209-673-5009

Modesto Chamber of Commerce,
Agribusiness Division
P.O. Box 844, Modesto 95353
Gary Dietrich, Director Govt. Affairs
209-577-5757

NAMA Cal (National Agri-Marketing Association)
12121 Wilshire Blvd., Los Angeles 90025
Lucinda S. Bacon, President
213-444-7000

NAMA West (National Agri-Marketing Association)
201 California Street, San Francisco 94111
Joe Robertson
415-616-6157

National Farmers Organization
Regional Marketing Office
415 E. Birch St., Hanford 93230
Ron Mattos
209-582-7292

Nor-Cal NAMA (National Agri-Marketing Association)
2640 Cordova Lane, Ste. 110,
Rancho Cordova 95670
Arthur J. Sainz, Jr., President
916-635-3828

Oxnard Pest Control Association/
Beneficial Insects
P.O. Box 1187, Oxnard 93032
Norman E. Frost, Jr., Manager
805-483-1024

People's Organization for Land Preservation
(P.O.L.P.)
P.O. Box 447, Linden 95236
John Eilers, President
209-887-3937

Pesticide Applicators Professional Association (PAPA)
4809 Michelle, Union City 94587
Dean Nissen, President
510-657-0693

San Joaquin Valley NAMA (National Agri-Marketing Association)
P.O. Box 5473, Fresno 93755
J. Michael Hurley, President
209-233-7249

Southland Farmers' Market Association
1010 South Flower St., Room 402
Los Angeles 90015
Marion Kalb, Director
213-749-9551

SRI International
333 Ravenswood Ave., Menlo Park 94025
John L. Bomben, Ph.D., Director of Food & Agri-Business Program
415-326-6200   FAX 415-326-5512

Steering Committee for Sustainable Agriculture (SCSA)
P.O. Box 1300, Colfax 95713
Otis Wollan, Executive Director
916-346-2777

Stockton Ag Expo
c/o Greater Stockton Chamber of Commerce
445 W. Weber, Suite 220, Stockton 95203
Olive Davis, Expo Manager
209-466-7066   FAX 209-466-5271

Tri Valley Growers
1255 Battery St., San Francisco 94111
P.O. Box 7114, San Francisco 94120-7114
Travis H. Mullenix, President/Chief Officer
415-445-1600   FAX 415-445-1628 or 1660

United Agribusiness League
54 Corporate Park, Irvine 92714
Bill Goodrich, President
714-975-1424

Ventura County Agricultural Association
P.O. Box 1388, Oxnard 93032
Robert P. Roy, President
805-485-7911

Western Agricultural Chemicals Association
930 G Street, Ste. 210
Sacramento 95814
Steve Forsberg, Executive Director
916-446-9222   FAX 916-446-4703

Western Fairs Association
1329 Howe Ave., Ste. 202, Sacramento 95825
Stephen Chambers, Executive Director
916-927-3100

Western Growers Association
17620 Fitch St., Irvine 92714
David L. Moore, President
714-863-1000   FAX 714-863-9028
1005-12th St., Ste. A, Sacramento 95814
916-446-1435   FAX 916-446-0181

Western Society of Weed Science
P.O. Box 963, Newark 94560
Wanda Graves, Business Manager
510-793-4169

Livestock and Dairy

GENERAL

Grand National Foundation
5-3rd St., Ste. 200 Hearst Building, San Francisco 94103
N. Stevens, Executive Director
415-777-0600 or 415-922-4062

Producers Livestock Marketing Association
867 W. 32nd St., Yuma, AZ 85364
Faris Sommers, Manager
602-726-6827

Producers Livestock Marketing Association
13314 Rd. 26, P.O. Box 510, Madera 93639
Clif Calhoun, Manager
209-674-4674

Western Brahman Breeders Association
16533 Escalon Bellota Rd., Escalon, 95320
Dennis Wilson, President
209-838-3153

Western States Meat Association
P.O. Box 12944, Oakland 94604
1615 Broadway, Ste. 900, Oakland 94612
Rosemary Mucklow, Executive Director
510-763-1533

BEES AND HONEY

California State Beekeepers Association
19980 Pine Creek Road, Red Bluff 96080
Carol Penner, Secretary
916-527-0941

Sioux Honey Association
P.O. 668, Anaheim 92805
Carl Kayl, Plant Manager
714-776-4112

CATTLE

National Cattlemen's Association
P.O. Box 3469, Englewood, CO 80155
J. Burton Eller, Executive Vice President
303-694-0305

California Beef Cattle Improvement Association
　1605 L. Honcut Road, Oroville 95966
　Cindy Daley, Secretary/Treasurer
　916-749-1705

California Cattlemen's Association
　1221 H Street, Sacramento 95814
　John L. Braly, Executive Vice President
　916-444-0845　　FAX 916-325-9355

California Cattlemen's Association Feeder Council
　1221 H St., Sacramento 95814
　John Braly, Secretary
　916-444-0845

Member County Associations:

Amador-El Dorado-Sacramento Cattlemen's Association
　P.O. Box 1021, Ione 95640
　Laurie Forster, Secretary/Treasurer
　209-274-4606

Butte County Cattlemen's Association
　784 Flag Creek Rd., Oroville 95965
　Dave Scheuermann, Secretary
　916-533-5951

Calaveras-Tuolumne Cattlemen's Association
　P.O. Box 997, Angels Camp 95221
　Rex Whittle, Secretary/Treasurer
　209-736-0234

Contra Costa-Alameda Cattlemen's Association
　5554 Clayton Rd., Concord 94521
　Susan Spannagel, Secretary
　510-672-5116

Fall River-Big Valley Cattlemen's Association
　P.O. Box 151, McArthur 96056
　Ernest Bruce, Secretary/Treasurer
　916-336-5187

Fresno-Kings Cattlemen's Association
　3650 N. Bethel, Sanger 93657
　Sally Behling, Secretary
　209-875-0255

Glenn-Colusa Cattlemen's Association
　P.O. Box 213, Willows 95988
　Andrea Feeney, Secretary/Treasurer
　916-934-9860

High Desert Cattlemen's Association
　32322 Hinkley Rd., Barstow 92311
　Ann Mitchell, Secretary/Treasurer
　619-253-2359

Humboldt-Del Norte Cattlemen's Association
　Fort Baker Ranch, Kneeland 95549
　Peggy Rice, Secretary
　707-777-3240

Inyo-Mono-Alpine Cattlemen's Association
　R.R.1.-100 Warm Springs Rd., Bishop 93514
　Alonna Giacomini, Secretary
　805-873-5135

Kern County Cattlemen's Association
　Star Route 3 Box 43-Granite Station
　Bakersfield 93301
　Jack Davidson, Secretary/Treasurer
　805-393-5459

Lake County Cattlemen's Association
　P.O. Box 198, Kelseyville 95451
　Jeff Gleaves, Secretary/Treasurer
　707-987-0124

Lassen County Cattlemen's Association
　702-535 Johnstonville Rd., Susanville 96130
　Mike Bartley, Secretary/Treasurer
　916-257-8958

Madera County Cattlemen's Association
　P.O. Box 721, Madera 93639
　Jeanne Todisco, Secretary/Treasurer
　209-674-0195

Mendocino County Cattlemen's Association
　24777 East Lane, Covelo 95428
　Edwin Phillips, Secretary/Treasurer
　707-983-6203

Merced-Mariposa Cattlemen's Association
　P.O. Box 1001, Merced 95341
　Jim Farley, Secretary/Treasurer
　209-385-7403

Modoc County Cattlemen's Association
　202 W. 4th Street, Alturas 96101
　Cathy Baldwin, Secretary
　916-233-3939

Monterey County Cattlemen's Association
　Lone Oak Rd., Box 51, King City 93930
　Susan Nino, Secretary
　408-385-6410

Napa-Solano Cattlemen's Association
　6760 Pleasants Valley Road, Vacaville 95688
　Silvio Pelandini, Secretary/Treasurer
　707-448-4292

Plumas-Sierra Cattlemen's Association
　Box 64, Sattley 96124
　Barbara Turner, Secretary/Treasurer
　916-994-3310

San Benito County Cattlemen's Association
　1871 Los Viboras, Hollister 95023
　Jeff Bourdet, Secretary/Treasurer
　408-623-2121

San Diego-Imperial Cattlemen's Association
26040 Mesa Grande Track Trail
Santa Ysabel 92070
Carolyn Alford, Secretary
619-742-3213

San Joaquin-Stanislaus Cattlemen's Association
265 California Ave., Oakdale 95361
William Fogarty, Secretary/Treasurer
209-847-5271

San Luis Obispo County Cattlemen's Association
P.O. Box 4157, San Luis Obispo 93403
JoAnn Switzer, Secretary/Treasurer
805-543-5463

San Mateo-San Francisco Cattlemen's Association
P.O. Box 527, Pescadero 94060
Merritt Moore, Secretary/Treasurer
415-879-0390

Santa Barbara County Cattlemen's Association
P.O. Box 617, Los Alamos 93440
Bill King, Secretary
805-344-3351

Santa Clara County Cattlemen's Association
P.O. Box 1721, Gilroy 95021
John Scherrer, Secretary
408-842-2932

Santa Cruz County Cattlemen's Association
959 Riverside, Watsonville 95076
Margaret Gnehm, Secretary/Treasurer
408-724-0974

Shasta County Cattlemen's Association
880 Hallmark Dr., Redding 96001
Walt Johnson, Secretary
916-241-6372

Siskiyou County Cattlemen's Association
3501 Hoy Rd., Weed 96094
Bill Hoy, Secretary/Treasurer
916-938-2110

Sonoma-Marin Cattlemen's Association
4180 Sonoma Mtn. Rd., Santa Rosa 95404
Pat Noren, Secretary/Treasurer
707-542-4030

Southern California Cattlemen's Association
3121 Mulberry St., Riverside 92501
Merritt Maddox, Secretary
714-686-7555

Tahoe Cattlemen's Association
6700 Garden Bar Rd., Lincoln 95648
Jerry Van Rein, Secretary
916-645-7666

Tehama County Cattlemen's Association
21495 Wilcox Rd., Red Bluff 96080
Bert Owens, Secretary
916-527-4900

Tulare County Cattlemen's Association
29180 Road 168, Visalia, 93277
Jo-Wayne Lyons, Secretary
209-627-3022

Ventura County Cattlemen's Association
P.O. Box 538, Somis 93066
John S. Harvey, Secretary/Treasurer
805-386-4255

Yolo County Cattlemen's Association
Rt. 1, Box 88, Arbuckle 95912
Cheryl Howard, Secretary
916-476-3338

Yuba-Sutter Cattlemen's Association
2689 Colusa Hwy., Yuba City 95991
Leonard Henson, Secretary/Treasurer
916-674-0776

California Nevada Hereford Association
Box 72, Vinton 96135
Vicki Paxton, Secretary
916-993-4216

California-Nevada Polled Hereford Association
8500 Rock Springs Rd., Penryn 95663
Karen Perrin, Secretary
916-663-1142

North Coast Livestock Protective Association
P.O. Box 6674, Santa Rosa 95406
Jerry Corda, President
707-544-5575

Red Bluff Bull and Gelding Sale
P.O. Box 930, Red Bluff 96080
Tyler Martinez, Manager
916-527-2045

DAIRY

Alliance of Western Milk Producers
1315 K Street, Modesto 95354
Jim Tillison, Chief Executive Officer
209-527-6453   FAX 209-527-0630

Associated Independent Dairies of America
502 Mace Blvd., Ste. 12, Davis 95616
Larry Maes, Manager
916-756-3969

California Creamery Operators Association
502 Mace Blvd., Ste. 12
Davis 95616
Larry Maes, Secretary/Treasurer
916-756-3969

California Cooperative Creamery
P.O. Box 871, Petaluma 94953
Michael E. Nash, Chief Executive Officer
707-763-1931   FAX 707-778-2343

California Dairy Herd Improvement Association
4942 E. Yale, Ste. 103, Fresno 93727
Bill Verboort, General Manager
209-255-1300   FAX 209-255-2106

County Dairy Herd Improvement Associations:

Arcata DHIA
5630 S. Broadway, Eureka 95501

Central Coast Counties DHIA
P.O. Box 3916, Salinas 93912

Churchill DHIA
5780 Candee Lane, Fallon, NV 89406
Evelyn King

Del Norte DHIA
2801 Lake Earl Drive, Cresent City 95531
Ernie Silva

Douglas DHIA
835 Whitney Way, Gardnerville, NV 89410
Archie Reed

El Dorado DHIA
2446 E. Washington St., Petaluma 94952
Myra Bamberger

Ferndale Cow Testing Association
P.O. Box 1308, Ferndale 95536
Richard Nicolds

Fresno County DHIA
2563 S. Sarah, Fresno 93706
Ed Soares

Glenn County DHIA
722 Fifth St., Orland 95963
Harvey Moranda

Kings County DHIA
870 Greenfield Ave., Hanford 93230
Ed Vink

Merced County DHIA
1520 W. Main, Merced 95340

North Bay DHIA
P.O. Box 233, Petaluma 94953
Mike Haley, Manager

North Central Valley DHIA
10557 S. Stockton Blvd., Elk Grove 95624
Lewis Lindsay

Placer-Nevada DHIA
7920 El Verano Ave., Elverta 95626
Howard Sheldon

San Joaquin County DHIA
1801 W. Euclid, Stockton 95204
James Lowe, Manager

Southern Counties DHIA
7000 Merrill Ave., Chino 91710
Rick Bealer, Manager

Stainslaus DHIA
725B N. Tully Rd., Turlock 95380
Harry Thompson

Tehama DHIA
P.O. Box 370, Red Bluff 96080
Arie Poldervaart

Tulare DHIA
253 S. I Street, Tulare 93274
Charles Latham, Manager

Virgin Valley DHIA
P.O. Box 126, Logandale, NV 89021
Ray Blackwell

California Holstein Association
1177 West Hedges, Fresno 93728
William J. Zinn, President
209-441-1206   FAX 209-441-1268

California Milk Producers
11709 East Artesia Blvd., Artesia 90701
Gary Korsmeier, Chief Executive Officer
310-865-1291   FAX 310-860-6543

Challenge Dairy Products, Inc.
P.O. Box 2369, Dublin 94568
John Whetten, President
510-828-6160

Consolidated Milk Producers of Kings County
870 Greenfield Ave., Hanford 93230
Kelly Maytubby, Executive Secretary
209-584-3557

Dairy Institute of California
1127 11th St., Suite 718, Sacramento 95814
Robert Boynton, Executive Director
916-441-6921   FAX 916-441-0802

Dairyman's Cooperative Creamery Association
400 South "M" Street, Tulare 93274
Jimmie D. Prince, Chief Executive Officer
209-685-6800   FAX 209-685-6911

Danish Creamery Association
P.O. Box 11865, Fresno 93775
J.A. Gomes, President and
Chief Executive Officer
209-233-5154   FAX 209-268-5101

Glenn Milk Producers Association
P.O. Box 868, Willows 95988
Harvey Moranda, President
916-934-4671

Milk Producers Council
13545 Euclid Avenue, Ontario 91761
Robert Feenstra, General Manager
714-628-6018

San Joaquin Valley Dairymen
P.O. Box 2198, Los Banos 93635
John Aalberts, General Manager
209-826-4901

Western United Dairymen
1315 K Street, Modesto 95354
Ray Veldhuis, President
Richard Cotta, Executive Vice President/
Manager
209-527-6453   FAX 209-527-0630

FISH AND SHELLFISH

California Aquaculture Association
P.O. Box 1004, Niland 92257
George Ray, Secretary
619-359-3474

GOATS

California Dairy Goat Marketing Association
P.O. Box 457, Lincoln 95648
Chuck Wing, Secretary/Treasurer
916-645-8606

Dairy Goat Herd Improvement Association (DGHIA)
4942 E. Yale, Ste. 103, Fresno 93727
Bill Verboort, General Manager
209-255-1300   FAX 209-255-2106

Northern California DGHIA
Box 86, Igo 96047
Barbara Harrison

Southern Counties DGHIA
4239 Corona, Norco 91760
Bill Thomas

HOGS

California Pork Producers
3425 Jackie St., Visalia 93277
David Sharp, President
209-688-2051

San Joaquin Livestock Marketing Inc.
9641 Ave., 384, Dinuba 93618
Lee Kirkpatrick, Manager
209-591-0884

HORSES

American Buckskin Registry Association, Inc.
P.O. Box 3850, Redding 96049
Georgi Jones, Office Manager
Frieda Webb, Executive Secretary
916-223-1420

American Mule Association
1464 Beulah St., Hanford 93230
Bernita Garcia, Secretary
209-584-4214

California Dressage Society
P.O. Box 417, Carmel Valley 93924
Paula Langan, Manager
408-659-5696

California Horse Racing Board
1010 Hurley Way, Rm. 190, Sacramento 95825
Roy Minami, Assistant Secretary
916-920-7178   FAX 916-920-7658

California State Horsemen's Association
897 3rd Street, Santa Rosa 95404
Carol Overall, Secretary
707-544-2250

California Thoroughbred Breeders Association
201 Colorado Place, Arcadia 91007-2604
P.O. Box 750, Arcadia 91066-0750
John Harris, President
818-445-7800   FAX 818-574-0852

Cal-Western Appaloosa Racing, Inc.
3097 Willow Avenue #15, Clovis 93612
Pam Haskell, Office Manager
209-291-0103

International Arabian Horse Association
P.O. Box 33696, Denver, CO 80233
303-450-4774   FAX 303-450-5127

Marin Horse Council
171 Bel Marin Keys Blvd., Novato 94949-6183
415-883-4621, ext. 361

Pacific Coast Quarter Horse Association
P.O. Box 254822, Sacramento 95865
916-922-9857

Pacific Racing Association
c/o Golden Gate Field
Box 6027, Albany 94706-0027
510-526-3020

West Coast Reining Horse Association, Inc.
10651 Wilton Rd., Elk Grove 95624
Judy Carpenter, Treasurer
916-686-6398

Woodland Stallion Station
Rt. 3, Box 623, Woodland 9; 595
Ann Taylor, General Partne
916-661-1358

POULTRY

California Poultry Health Board
3117-A McHenry Ave., Modesto 95350
Bill Mattos, Executive Director
209-576-6355   FAX 209-576-6119

California Poultry Industry Federation
3117-A McHenry Ave., Modesto 95350
Bill Mattos, Executive Director
209-576-6355   FAX 209-576-6119

Nulaid Foods, Inc.
200 West 5th St., Ripon 95366
Jeff Ovadia, President
209-599-2121

PCA Feed and Supply, Inc.
1863 Service Court, Riverside 92507
P.O. Box 626, Riverside 92502
Iva Rooker, General Manager
714-686-5272

Pacific Egg and Poultry Association
1620 N. Carpenter Rd., Ste. A4
Modesto 95351-1153
209-524-9666

San Bernardino Valley Egg Producers Association
280 South Palm, P.O. Box 71
Rialto 92376
Victor Clotts, President/Manager
Karen Connell, Secretary
714-820-9095

Squab Producers of California
409 Primo Way, Modesto 95351
R.E. Shipley, General Manager
209-537-4744

Sunshine Foods
9490 Edison, Chino 91710
Willard J. Maust, President
714-947-3551

Vitagold Brands Cooperative Association
135 S. Quince St., Escondido 92025
Richard I. Magoffin, General Manager
619-745-3211   FAX 619-745-3218

West Coast United Egg Producers
Box 1526, Rancho Cucamonga 91729
714-980-5114   FAX 714-945-3575

SHEEP

American Sheep Industry Association
6911 S. Yosemite St., Englewood, CO 80112
John M. Olson, Executive Director
303-771-3500

California Wool Growers Association
1221 H St., Ste. 101, Sacramento 95814-1910
Jay Wilson, Executive Vice President
916-444-8122

Branch Wool Growers Associations

Alameda County Wool Growers Association
P.O. Box 487, Pleasanton 94566
Al Spotorno
510-846-2396

Central California Wool Growers Association
2606 Benjamin Holt Drive, Stockton 95207
Florence Cubiburu
209-447-7765

Glenn-Colusa County Wool Growers Association
P.O. Box 627, Willows 95988
Dick Sexton
916-934-5748

Humboldt County Wool Growers Association
Bunkerhill Ranch, Ferndale 95536
Karen Russ
707-786-9239

Kern County Wool Growers Association
P.O. Box 5306, Oildale 93388
Paco Iturriria
805-399-5994

Mendocino County Wool Growers Association
P.O. Box 24, Manchester 95459
Darrell DePaul
707-877-3458

North Bay Wool Growers Association
1480 Bohemian Hwy, Sebastopol 95472
Donna Furlong
707-874-2777

Northern California Counties Wool Growers Association
P.O. Box 2314, Flournoy 96029
Lourence Alvares
916-824-3348

Solano County Wool Growers Association
P.O. Box 430, Dixon 95620
Ann Vassar
916-678-2340

Yolo County Wool Growers Association
Box 172, Zamora 95698
Ted Long
916-662-8333

Cal-Wool Marketing Association
P.O. Box 1108, Stockton 95201
Ernest Gutzman, General Manager
209-466-6866

Western Range Association
7844 Madison Avenue, Ste 105
Fair Oaks 95628
Larry Garro, Executive Director
916-962-1500   FAX 916-962-1626

Field Crops

BEANS

Cal-Bean and Grain Cooperative, Inc.
Drawer D, Pixley 93256
Don Cameron, Manager
209-757-3581

California Bean Growers Association
P.O. Box 24610, Ventura 93002
David Billings, President
805-652-0683   FAX 805-652-0430

Chico Bean Growers
4936 Bell Rd., Chico 95926
Michael D. Brown, Manager
916-343-1941

Greenville Warehouse
3232 Greenville Street, Santa Ana 92704
Hal Segerstrom, President
714-545-1922

Jojoba Southwest, Inc.
3911 N. Cordoba Ave., Ste. L
Spring Valley 91977
Dennis Slavens, President & Marketing Director
619-660-7322   FAX 619-660-9670

Stockton District Kidney Bean Growers, Inc.
P.O. Box 654, Linden 95236
Robert Maulhardt, Manager
209-887-3420   FAX 209-887-2107

West Stanislaus Growers Association
P.O. Box 38, Westley 95387
Doyle Wallace, Gen. Manager
209-894-3121   FAX 209-894-3457

COTTON AND COTTON GINS

Alta Vista Gin
5854 S. San Diego Avenue, Mendota 93640
Lloyd Hendrickson, Superintendent
209-655-3370 or 209-655-3221

AMCOT
P.O. Box 259, Bakersfield 93302
805-327-5961

Broadview Co-op Gin, Inc.
P.O. Box 186, Firebaugh 93622
Kenneth Rowan, Manager
209-659-1493   FAX 209-659-1518

Bullard Ginning Company
47375 West Dakota, Firebaugh 93622
William Nicholas, Manager
209-364-6185   FAX 209-364-6191

CALCOT, Ltd.
P.O. Box 259, Bakersfield 93302-0259
Tom W. Smith, President
805-327-5961   FAX 805-861-9870

California Cotton Ginners Association
1900 North Gateway Blvd., Ste 156
Fresno 93727
Kenneth B. Smith, Executive Vice President
209-252-0684   FAX 209-252-0551

California Planting Cotton Seed Distributors
P.O. Box 1281, Bakersfield 93302
2816 "K" Street, Bakersfield 93301
Tom Cherry, Manager/Treasurer
805-324-9858   FAX 805-324-5312

Calolina Ginning Company
P.O. Box 80007, Bakersfield 93380
Kenny Davis, Manager
805-399-5511   FAX 805-393-6744

Cantua Co-op Gin
P.O. Box 130, Cantua Creek 93608
Carlton Truhett, Manager
209-829-3321   FAX 209-829-6259

Caruthers Co-op Gin, Inc.
5391 W. Lincoln, Fresno 93706
Sally Gomez, Manager
209-237-6336

Central Valley Co-op
9845 Hanford Armona Rd., Hanford 93230
Leroy Goble, Manager
209-582-0321   FAX 209-582-9633

Church-Borchard-Murphy
P.O. Box 112, Brawley 92227
Jerry Moore, Manager
619-344-2432

Coalinga Farmers Co-op Gin, Inc.
P.O. Box 557, Coalinga 93210
Ewel Hudson, Jr., Manager
209-935-0282

Coit Ginning Company
2578 S. Lyon Avenue, Mendota 93640
Craig T. Ulrici, Manager
209-655-3632

Cotton Associates, Inc.
P.O. Bin 1268, Shafter 93263
R.J. Vignola, Manager
805-325-8243 or 805-746-2148
FAX 805-746-3643

County Line Gin, Inc.
12095 2nd Avenue, Hanford 93230
Mark Boyes, Manager
209-584-7489 or 209-733-4855
FAX 209-733-2038

CRS Ginning Company
P.O. Box 788, Shafter 93263
Bob Pacciorini, Manager
805-746-4470 or 805-797-2332

Dos Palos Co-op Gin, Inc.
7870 W. Hutchins Road, Dos Palos 93620
Bill Wilson, Manager
209-387-4151   FAX 209-387-4373

Eagle Field Ginning Co.
27480 S. Bennett Rd., Firebaugh 93622
Chuck West, Manager
209-364-6162

Eastcardale Co-op Gin, Inc.
P.O. Box 247, Kingsburg 93631
Mary Johnson, Manager
209-897-2429 or 209-591-1682

Elbow Enterprises, Inc.
1201 Avenue 328, Visalia 93291
Bob Faris, Manager
209-734-1177 or 209-734-1178

Farmers Co-op Gin, Inc.
2531 Wasco Way, Buttonwillow 93206
Michael Hooper, Manager
805-764-5251 or 805-764-5252
FAX 805-764-6600

Golden State Co-op Gins
P.O. Box 87, Madera 93637
Michael Gendron, Manager
209-674-5621

Growers' Westmorland Gin
Box 448, Westmorland 92281
Frank Cooley, Manager
619-344-1331

H & H Ginning
Route 1, Box 470, Coalinga 93210
R.G. "Skeet" Trapnell, Manager
209-884-2401   FAX 209-884-2891

Huron Ginning Company
P.O. Box 447, Huron 93234
Alford L. Albertson, Manager
209-945-2201 or 209-945-2202
FAX 209-945-2854

Island Co-op Gin, Inc.
20509 Elgin Avenue, Lemoore 93245
W.F. "Bill" Smyers, Manager
209-924-2969

Kerman Co-op Gin & Warehouse, Inc.
P.O. Box 396, Kerman 93630
Harold Hamilton, Manager
209-846-7307 or 209-266-7941
FAX 209-846-7308

Kern Delta-Weedpatch Cotton Ginning Co.
7809 Bear Mountain Blvd.
Bakersfield 93313-9109
David Alderete, Manager
805-831-2834

Kern Lake Co-op Gin
23727 Ashe Road, Bakersfield 93313
Gary Frisbee, Manager
805-858-2831

Laton Co-op Gin, Inc.
P.O. Box 128, Laton 93242
Joe F. Cotta, Manager
209-923-4943   FAX 209-923-4628

Madera Co-op Gin, Inc.
12501 Road 19, Madera 93637
Earl Martin, Manager
209-674-8849

McFarland Co-op Gin, Inc.
P.O. Box 428, McFarland 93250
Stephen Taylor, Manager
805-792-3134   FAX 805-792-3273

Mid-Valley Cotton Growers, Inc.
P.O. Box 901, Tulare 93275
Stan Creelman, Manager
209-686-2823   FAX 209-685-1550

Minturn Cooperative Gin, Inc./Minturn-Red Top
9158 S. Minturn Road, Chowchilla 93610
C.D. Johnson, Manager
209-665-4802 or 209-665-2024

Modern Ginning Company
P.O. Box 837, Blythe 92226
Loyd E. Colbert, Manager
619-922-0381

Mt. Whitney Ginning Co.
P.O. Box 305, Five Points 93624
Matt Diener, Manager
209-884-2161   FAX 209-884-2648

Panoche Ginning Co., Inc.
43890 North Ave., Firebaugh 93622
Ed Wandzell, Manager
209-659-1427

Planters Ginning Co./Weist Gin
P.O. Box 577, Westmorland 92281
Robert Bedwell, Manager
619-334-0620 or 619-348-2646

Raisin City Co-op Gin, Inc.
P.O. Box 114, Raisin City 93652
Dick Adams, Manager
209-268-1869   FAX 209-864-8208

Ranchers Cotton Oil
P.O. Box 2596, Fresno 93745
Glen Janzen, President
209-443-5270   FAX 209-443-5286

Richland Co-op Gin, Inc.
P.O. Box 1445, Shafter 93263
Gary Bailey, Manager
805-746-2933 or 805-323-8517
FAX 805-746-4613

Ridge Ginning Co.
P.O. Box 79158, Bakersfield 93381
Mary Jackson, Office Manager
805-858-2097 or 805-858-2007

**Ripley Ginning Corp./
Ripley Ginning L/S**
P.O. Box 548, Ripley 92272
Wallace Shropshire, Manager
619-922-8179 or 619-922-8170
FAX 619-922-5635

Semi-Tropic Co-op
25382 Hwy 46, Wasco 93280
Don Van Schuyver, Manager
805-758-5501   FAX 805-758-3016

Shafter-Wasco Ginning Co.
P.O. Box 1566, Shafter 93263
Tut Anderson, Manager
805-746-6321

South Valley Gin, Inc.
9759 Valpredo Rd., Bakersfield 93313
Joe Clark, Manager
805-858-2477 or 805-858-2031

Stratford Growers
P.O. Box 68, Stratford 93266
Joe Vierra, Manager
209-947-3072
FAX 209-947-9031 (Call first)

Tri-City Growers, Inc.
18897 Avenue 96, Terra Bella 93270
Rosemarie Dowdle, Manager
209-784-0142   FAX 209-784-1038

Tule River Cooperative
P.O. Box 4477, Woodville 93258
Mark Cartwright, Manager
209-686-4685   FAX 209-686-8061

Visalia Co-op Cotton Gin, Inc.
P.O. Box 1208, Visalias 93277
Larry Gallian Manager
209-732-1365 or 209-732-1485

Western Cotton Growers Association
1900 N. Gateway Blvd., Ste. 156, Fresno 93727
K.B. Smith, Executive Vice President
209-252-0688   FAX 209-252-0551

Westhaven Cotton Co.
P.O. Box 146, Stratford 93266-0146
Tom Pires, Manager
209-947-3185

Westlake Farms, Inc.
23311 Newton Ave., Stratford 93266
Ed Howe, Manager
209-947-3328   FAX 209-947-3590

Westside Farmers Coop Gin, Inc.
P.O. Box 558, San Joaquin 93660
Fred Cook, Manager
209-698-7221

West Valley Cotton Growers, Inc.
10030 W. Mt. Whitney, Riverdale 93656
Thomas Pires, Manager
209-866-5351 or 209-866-5384

Wheeler Farms
34741 7th Standard Rd., Bakersfield 93312
Becky Shelton, Manager
805-399-9121   FAX 805-399-9274

GRAIN

California Association of Wheat Growers
P.O. Box 209, Woodland 95695
Daniel M. Weldon, Executive Vice President
916-666-5472   FAX 916-483-5889

California Grain and Feed Association
1715 Capitol Ave., Sacramento 95814
Richard Matteis, Executive Vice President
916-441-2272   FAX 916-446-1063

Imperial Grain Growers, Inc.
P.O. Box 184, Brawley 92227
Mike Thomas, Manager
619-344-0420   FAX 619-344-1309

Newell Grain Growers Association
P.O. Box 576, Tulelake 96134
Ronald K. Greenbank, Manager
916-667-2603

**San Luis Obispo County Farm Bureau
Grain Improvement Association**
651 Tank Farm Road, San Luis Obispo 93401
Steve Hansen, President
805-543-3654

Southwest Marketing Corporation
P.O. Box 1027, Imperial 92251
Rob Huntington, President
619-352-3251   FAX 619-355-2594

Western Grain Marketing, Inc.
P.O. Box 7316, Stockton 95267
John M. Stevens, General Manager
209-931-0883

HAY

Kern County Hay Growers Association
14125 Castajo Rd., Bakersfield 93313
Truman Brown, Manager
805-831-2302

San Joaquin Valley Hay Growers Association
P.O. Box 1127, Tracy 95378
M. Mel Coelho, Manager, Executive Secretary
209-835-1662   FAX 209-835-0719

POTATOES

Gold Ribbon Potato Company
P.O. Box 197, Arvin 93203
Howard Frick, President
805-854-4421   FAX 805-854-3805

Newell Potato Cooperative, Inc.
P.O. Box 851, Tulelake 96134
John Cross, Manager
916-664-2591 or 916-664-2881

RICE

Butte County Rice Growers Association
Box 128, Richvale 95974
John Valpey, Manager
916-882-4261   FAX 916-882-4580

California Rice Industry Association
701 University Ave., Ste. 205
Sacramento 95825-6708
Ralph S. Newman, Chairman
916-929-3996   FAX 916-929-0732

Farmers' Rice Cooperative
P.O. Box 15223, Sacramento 95851-0223
2525 Natomas Park Drive, Ste. 300
Sacramento 95833
Ralph S. Newman, Jr., President
916-923-5100   FAX 916-920-4295

Red Top Rice Growers
P.O. Box 477, Biggs 95917
Paul De Meyer, President
916-868-5975

Rice Growers Association of California
P.O. Box 958, Sacramento 95812-0958
David R. Long, Chief Executive Officer
916-371-6941

Sutter Basin Growers Cooperative
P.O. Box 355, Knights Landing 95645
Stephen Haskell, General Manager
916-735-6295   FAX 916-735-6297

SUGAR

California & Hawaiian Sugar Company, (C&H)
1390 Willow Pass Rd., Ste. 700, Concord 94520
Harold R. Somerset, President &
Chief Executive Officer
510-356-6000

California Beet Growers Association, Ltd.
2 West Swain Road, Stockton 95207
Ben Goodwin, Executive Manager
209-477-5596   FAX 209-477-1610

Fruits and Nuts

American Frozen Food Institute
1838 El Camino Real, Ste. 202
Burlingame 94010
Jean Bohannan, Senior Vice President,
Convention Services
415-697-6835   FAX 415-697-6646

Atwater Fruit Exchange
P.O. Box 754, Atwater 95301
Ted J. Moschitto, President
209-358-2272

Blue Anchor, California Fruit Exchange
730 Howe Avenue, Sacramento 95825
Patrick Sanguinetti, President
916-929-3050   FAX 916-921-9362

Bovetti Packing
P.O. Box 196, Exeter 93221
Phil Bovetti, Manager
209-592-3191

California Fresh Fruit Growers, Inc.
5108 E. Clinton Way, Ste. 115, Fresno 93727
Harry Kubo, President
209-251-8468

California Fuyu Growers Association
P.O. Box 1301, Valley Center 92082
Charley J. Wolk, Jr., President
619-723-1620

California Grape and Tree Fruit League
1540 East Shaw Avenue, Ste 120
Fresno 93710-8000
Michael Durando, President
209-226-6330   FAX 209-222-8326

Diamond Walnut Growers, Inc.
P.O. Box 1727, Stockton 95201
William Cuff, President
209-467-6000

Farmers Cold Storage and Freezers, Inc.
274 Kearney, Watsonville 95076
Ray Rodriguez, Manager
408-724-1144   FAX 408-728-0459

Foothill Properties
510 W. Chase Drive, Corona 91720
Charles W. Colladay, General Manager
714-737-6321   FAX 714-737-0718

Fruit Growers Laboratory, Inc.
853 Corporation Street, Santa Paula 93060
Darrell H. Nelson, President/Gen. Mgr.
805-659-0910   FAX 805-525-4172

Index Fresh of California
18184 Slover Ave., Bloomington 92316
M.A. Browne, President
714-877-1577

Landmark Produce Sales
P.O. Box D, Victor 95253
209-369-6475   FAX 209-334-0246

Livingston Farmers Association
P.O. Box 456, Livingston 95334
Tad Kurosaki, Chief Executive Officer
209-394-7941   FAX 209-394-7952

Loomis Fruit Growers Association
P.O. Box 505, Loomis 95650
Randy Hansen, Treasurer/Manager
916-652-7251

Mayflower Fruit Association
P.O. Box 308, Exeter 93221
John Dubendorf, President
209-592-3134   FAX 209-592-6247

Pacific Coast Producers
631 North Cluff, P.O. Box 1600
Lodi 95241-1600
Larry D. Clay, President
209-367-8800   FAX 209-339-8815

Placerville Fruit Growers Association
4600 Missouri Flat Road, Placerville 95667
Scott R. Huston, Manager
916-622-2640

Redlands Foothill Groves
304 Ninth St., Redlands 92374
Tim Farmer, General Manager
714-793-2164   FAX 714-798-0669

Royal Valley Fruit Growers Association
P.O. Box 152, Reedley 93654
Stuart Rotan, General Manager
209-638-2540 or 209-638-8540

San Antonio Orchard Company
P.O. Box 588, Ontario 91762
714-984-3612

Suisun Valley Fruit Growers Association
4163 Chadbourne Rd., P.O. Box 417
Suisun City 94585
Robert H. Hansen, Manager
707-425-2503

Sun Diamond Growers of California
P.O. Box 9024, Pleasanton 94566
Larry D. Busboom, President
510-463-8200   FAX 510-463-7492

APPLES

Apple Growers Ice & Cold Storage
P.O. Box 854, Watsonville 95077
Steve Zupan, President
408-724-1321

Apple Hill Growers
P.O. Box 494, Camino 95709
Dale Martin, President
916-622-7692

California Granny Smith Association
1941 Northgate Way Blvd., Ste. 102
Fresno 93727
Kenton Kidd, President
209-456-0900   FAX 209-456-0125

Sebastopol Apple Growers United
2060 Gravenstein Highway North
Sebastopol 95472
Dennis Walsh, Owner
707-823-7836   FAX 707-823-0624

APRICOTS

Apricot Producers of California
1064 Woodland Ave., Ste. E
Modesto 93351-1349
Barbara Watts, Vice President of Operations
209-524-0801   FAX 209-524-3840

AVOCADOS

Avocado Growers Association
365 W. Second Ave., Ste. 101
Escondido 92025-4136
Warren Currier, Executive Director
619-746-9600

Calavo Growers of California
15661 Red Hill Ave., Tustin 92680-7321
P.O. Box 26081, Santa Ana 92799-6081
Allen Vangelos, President
714-259-1166

BERRIES

Naturipe Berry Growers
P.O. Box A, Watsonville 95077
Herb Baum, President
408-722-2439   FAX 408-728-9398

Oxnard Berry Farm
P.O. Box 1295, Oxnard 93032
800 S. Rose Ave., Oxnard 93030
Thomas Oliva, President
805-483-0181

CHERRIES

California Cherry Export Association
P.O. Box 877, Lodi 95241
48 E. Oak, Lodi 95240
James Christie, Manager
209-368-0685   FAX 209-368-4309

California Cherry Growers & Industry Foundation
48 E. Oak Street, Lodi 95240
James Christie, Manager
209-368-0685   FAX 209-464-8575

San Joaquin Valley Cherry Shippers
P.O. Box 877, Lodi 95241
James C. Christie, Manager
209-368-0685   FAX 209-368-4309

CITRUS

California-Arizona Citrus League
25060 Avenue Stanford, Ste. 200
Valencia 91355-3446
805-257-3682

California Citrus Mutual
1110 E. Houston Ave., Visalia 93291
P.O. Box 687, 93279
Joel Nelsen, President
209-732-9177   FAX 209-732-6832

California Citrus Quality Council
953 W. Foothill Blvd., Claremont 91711
Paul B. Engler, Executive Secretary
714-621-2994   FAX 714-626-5895

Sunkist Growers, Inc.
14130 Riverside Drive, Sherman Oaks 91423-2392
P.O. Box 7888, Van Nuys 91409-7888
Russell L. Hanlin, President
818-986-4800   FAX 818-379-7204

Each of the more than 6,500 grower-members of Sunkist Growers, Inc. is also a member of a member local association or district exchange. Packing and shipping facilities are provided to growers either by local associations or by non-member licensed packers authorized by Sunkist Growers, Inc. and a district exchange to perform that service. The district exchanges and local associations, together with the licensed packers are:

Allied Citrus Exchange, Inc.
P.O. Box 15584, Phoenix, AZ 85060-5584

Mesa Citrus Growers
P.O. Box 1388, Mesa, AZ 85211

Production Farm Management, Inc.
P.O. Box 1029, Glendale, AZ 85311

Blue Banner Fruit Exchange
P.O. Box 1154, Riverside 92502

Blue Banner Company, Inc.
P.O. Box 226, Riverside 92502

Central California Citrus Exchange
P.O. Box 279, Lindsay 93247

Baker Bros.
P.O. Box 307, Woodlake 93286

Gillette Citrus Co.
10175 S. Anchor Ave., Dinuba 93618

Golden Valley Citrus, Inc.
P.O. Box L, Strathmore 93267

H & R Citrus
6748 S. Cove Ave.
Orange Cove 93646

Ivanhoe Citrus Association
P.O. Box 459, Ivanhoe 93235

Kaweah Citrus Assn. #1
P.O. Box 68, Lemon Cove 93244

Kaweah Citrus Assn. #2
P.O. Box 67, Orange Cove 93646

Lawson Packing
14085 Ave., 412, Orosi 93647

Lindsay Fruit Association
P.O. Box 930, Lindsay 93247

McKinney Packing, Inc.
46016 Road 128, Orange Cove 93646

Millwood Packing, Inc.
P.O. Box 278, Orange Cove 93646

Oxnard Lemon Company
P.O. Box 2240, Oxnard 93034

Sierra Citrus Association
P.O. Box 338, Lindsay 93247

Sierra Vista Packing Co., Inc.
P.O. Box 1, Orosi 93647

Stark Packing Corporation
P.O. Box 127, Strathmore 93267

Fillmore-Piru Citrus Exchange
P.O. Box 635, Fillmore 93016

Fillmore-Piru Citrus Association
P.O. Box 635, Fillmore, CA 93016

Mid-California Citrus Exchange
3326 W. Mineral King, Visalia 93291

Exeter Citrus Association
901 Rocky Hill Drive, Exeter 93221

Harding & Leggett Inc.
440 Anchor Ave., Orange Cove 93646

Klink Citrus Association
Box 188, Ivanhoe 93235

Orange Cove-Sanger Citrus Association
180 South Avenue, Orange Cove 93646

Orange County Fruit Exchange
Box 189, Orange 92666

Coachella Valley Citrus
P.O. Box 1065, Thermal 92274

Orange Heights Orange Association
Box 608, Corona 91718-0608

Redlands Foothill Groves
304 Ninth St., Redlands 92374

Riverside-Arlington Heights Fruit Exchange
Box 5625, Riverside 92517-5625

L.V.W. Brown Estate, Inc.
859 Center St., Highgrove 92507

National Orange Packing Company
3604 Commerce St., Riverside 92507

Richard Bagdassarian, Inc.
P.O. Box 698, Meca 92254

Yorba Orange Growers Association
P.O. Box 69, Anaheim 92815

Royal Citrus Exchange
P.O. Box 288, Riverside 92502

Royal Citrus Company
P.O. Box 288, Riverside 92502

Saticoy Fruit Exchange
P.O. Box 5180, Ventura 93005-5180

Saticoy Lemon Association
P.O. Box 46, Santa Paula 93061-0046

Southern Arizona Citrus Exchange
350 W. 16th, Ste. 304, Yuma, AZ 85364

Marlin Packing Company
P.O. Box 5839, Yuma, AZ 85366-5839

Yuma Mesa Fruit Growers Association
P.O. Box 2889, Yuma, AZ 85366-2889

Sun Pacific Exchange
P.O. Box 217, Exeter 93221

Sun Pacific Shippers, Inc.
P.O. Box 217, Exeter 93221

Tulare County Fruit Exchange
P.O. Box 231, Porterville 93258

Baird-Neece Packing Corporation
P.O. Box 791, Porterville 93258

Magnolia Citrus Association
P.O. Box 168, Porterville 93258

Paloma Citrus Association
35586 Road 180, Visalia 93291

Porterville Citrus Association, The
142 W. Olive Ave., Porterville 93257

Strathmore Cooperative Association
Drawer 277, Strathmore 93267

Strathmore Packing House Company
Box 368, Strathmore 93267

Sunland Packing House Company
26454 Ave. 128, Porterville 93257

Tulare, County Lemon Association
Box 1169, Porterville 93258

Tulare Kern Citrus Exchange
P.O. Box 55, Terra Bella 93270

Grand View Heights Citrus Association
9600 Road 256, Terra Bella 93270

Ventura County Citrus Exchange
P.O. Box 71, Santa Paula 93060

Mission Citrus
P.O. Box 6407, Yuma, AZ 85366-6407

Ojai-Tapo Citrus Association
P.O. Box 317, Somis 93066

Santa Paula Orange Association
P.O. Box 990, Santa Paula 93060

Ventura County Fruit Growers, Inc.
P.O. Box 307, Fillmore 93015

Ventura Pacific Company
P.O. Box 5599, Montalvo 93005

Ventura County Fruit Exchange
1141 Cummings Rd., Santa Paula 93060

Limoneira Company
1141 Cummings Rd.
Santa Paula 93060

Villa Park Citrus Exchange
P.O. Box 310, Orange 92666-0310

Villa Park Orchards Association, The
P.O. Box 339, Orange 92666

Visalia Fruit Exchange
P.O. Box 1111, Visalia 93279

Golden State Citrus Packers
P.O. Box 607, Woodlake 93286

Tri-County Citrus Association
12143 Ave. 456, Orange Cove 93646

Visalia Citrus Packers
P.O. Box 2800, Visalia 93279

Tri Citrus Association
23744 Ave. 181, Porterville 93257
Bruce Wileman, Manager
209-784-8820   FAX 209-784-1520

GRAPES AND COOPERATIVE WINERIES

Allied Grape Growers
3475 West Shaw Ave., Ste. 103
Fresno 93711
Barry J. Bedwell, President
209-276-7021

Beverage Source, Inc., The
10990 Wilshire Blvd., Ste. 1800
Los Angeles 90024
Richard McCombs, Exec. Vice President
213-312-9463   FAX 213-312-6899
2916 S. Reed Avenue, Sanger 93657
209-638-3511   FAX 209-638-8995

California Association of Winegrape Growers
77 Cadillac Dr., Ste. 100
Sacramento 95825
Robert Hartzell, President
916-920-9187   FAX 916-924-0904

California North Coast Grape Growers
P.O. Box 213, Ukiah 95482
James F. Forchini, President
707-462-1361

Delano Growers Grape Products
Route 1, Box 283, Delano 93215
Ray Cox, Administrative Manager
805-725-3255   FAX 805-725-0279

East-Side Winery
6100 East Highway 12, Lodi 95240
Gary Forberg, General Manager
209-369-4768   FAX 209-369-0202

Gibson Wine Company
1720 Academy Avenue, Sanger 93657
Rich Edwards, Vice President/
  General Manager
209-875-2505

Grape Improvement Association
P.O. Box 3070, Modesto 95353
Bill Brush, President
209-522-7278

Guild Wineries and Distilleries
Headquarters Office:
P.O. Box 55, Woodbridge 95258
Chris Kalabokes, President
209-368-5151
Marketing/Sales Office
391 Taylor Blvd., Ste. 10
Pleasant Hill 94523
510-798-7722

Bear Creek Winery
11900 North Furry Road, Lodi 95240
Ruben Negrete, Winery Manager
209-368-5151

Cribari Winery
P.O. Box 1068, Fresno 93714
Don Medina, Manager
209-485-3080

Mendocino Vineyards Winery
2399 North State Street, Ukiah 95482
George Phelan, Manager
707-462-2985

Lake County Grape Growers
65 Soda Bay Rd., Lakeport 95453
707-263-0911

Lodi District Grape Growers Association
P.O. Box 2004, Lodi 95241-2004
John Ledbetter, President
209-339-8246

Lodi District Vintners Association
P.O. Box 1398, Woodbridge 95258
Bill Wieland, President
209-239-1215

Mendocino County Vintners Association
P.O. Box 1409, Ukiah 95482
Tom Liden, Director
707-468-1343   FAX 707-468-1343

Monterey County Grape Growers Association
512 Pajaro St., Ste. 12, Salinas 93901
408-422-9063   FAX 408-422-9065

Monterey Wine Country Associates
P.O. Box 1793, Monterey 93942
David Armamasco, P R Director
408-375-9400   FAX 408-372-4142

Napa Valley Cooperative Winery
401 S. St. Helena Hwy.
St. Helena 94575
Kenneth V. Parr, President
707-963-2335   FAX 707-963-8537

Napa Valley Grape Growers
4075 Solano Ave., Napa 94558
Mary Handel, Executive Director
707-944-8311

Napa Valley Vintners Association
P.O. Box 141, St. Helena 94574
Elaine Mackie, Executive Director
707-963-0148   FAX 707-963-8432

Santa Clara Valley Winegrowers
P.O. Box 1192, Morgan Hill 95037
408-842-5649

Santa Cruz Mountain Vintners
P.O. Box 2856, Saratoga 95070
Robert Mullen, President
415-851-3144

Sonoma County Wineries Association
Luther Burbank Center for the Arts
50 Mark West Springs Rd., Santa Rosa 95403
Linda Johnson, Executive Director
707-527-7701   FAX 707-526-6645

Wine Institute
425 Market St., Ste. 1000, San Francisco 94105
John A. De Luca, President
415-512-0151   FAX 415-391-4269

Woodbridge Vineyard Association
P.O. Box 917, Woodbridge 95280-0917
Leonard V. Thompson, President
209-369-2614

KIWI

Kiwifruit Growers of California
7946 Pocket Rd., #18
Sacramento 95831
Ken Young, Manager
916-427-1544   FAX 916-399-1910

OLIVES

California Olive Association
c/o California League of Food Processors
1112 I Street, Ste. 100, Sacramento 95814
Bill Grigg, Secretary
916-444-9260   FAX 916-444-2746

Lindsay International, Inc.
650 W. Tulare Road, Lindsay 93247
Robert Rossio, President
209-562-5121   FAX 209-562-1620

Lindsay Olive Growers
P.O. Box 278, Lindsay 93247
Robert Rossio, President
209-562-5121   FAX 209-562-1620

Oberti Olives
12806 Road 26, Madera 93637
P.O. Box 899, Madera 93639
Gary Oberti, Sr. Vice President,
 Specialty Products
209-674-8741   FAX 209-673-3960

Olive Growers Council
121 E. Main St., Suite 8, Visalia 93291
Adin Hester, President
209-734-1710   FAX 209-625-4847

PEACHES

California Canning Peach Association
P.O. Box 7001, Lafayette 94549
Ronald A. Schuler, President
510-284-9171   FAX 510-284-4217

California Freestone Peach Association
P.O. Box 3004, Modesto 95353
Bill Bryan, Field Representative
209-538-2372   FAX 209-537-1043

PEARS

California Pear Growers
1600 Sacramento Inn Way, Ste. 229
Sacramento 95815
Jean-Mari Peltier, President
916-924-0530   FAX 916-924-0904

Kelseyville Packing Company
P.O. Box 335, Kelseyville 95451
Brian Dallas, Manager
707-279-4204   FAX 707-279-9417

Mt. Konocti Growers, Inc.
P.O. Box 365, Kelseyville 95451
Richard A. Barnett, Manager
707-279-4213   FAX 707-279-2251

Scotts Valley Fruit Exchange
P.O. Box 335, Lakeport 95453
Daniel S. Price, Manager
707-263-4495   FAX 707-263-1839

DRIED FRUITS

California Dried Fruit Export Association
303 Brokaw Road, Santa Clara 95050
P.O. Box 270-A, Santa Clara 95052
Frank A. Mosebar, Secretary/Treasurer
408-727-9302   FAX 408-970-3833

California Fig Institute
P.O. Box 709, Fresno 93712
Ron Klamm, Managing Director
209-224-3447   FAX 209-224-3449

Dried Fruit Association of California
303 Brokaw Rd., Santa Clara 95050
P.O. Box 270-A, Santa Clara 95052
Frank A. Mosebar, President
408-727-9302   FAX 408-970-3833

Fresno Cooperative Raisin Growers
    4466 North Dower Avenue, Fresno 93722
    Jerald Rebensdorf, President
    209-275-3710   FAX 209-275-3908

Raisin Bargaining Association
    3425 N. First St., Ste. 209
    Fresno 93726-6819
    Glen S. Goto, President
    209-221-1925

Sun-Diamond Growers of California
    P.O. Box 9024, Pleasanton 94566
    Larry D. Busboom, President
    510-463-8200   FAX 510-463-7492

Sun-Maid Growers of California
    13525 South Bethel Avenue, Kingsburg 93631
    Barry Kriebel, President and General Mgr.
    209-896-8000   FAX 209-897-2362

Valley Fig Growers
    P.O. Box 1987, Fresno 93718
    Jennifer Mathis, President
    209-237-3893   FAX 209-237-3898

PRUNES

Prune Bargaining Association
    P.O. Box 3398, Yuba City 95992
    Greg Thompson, General Manager
    916-674-5636

Sun-Diamond Growers of California
    P.O. Box 9020, Pleasanton 94566
    Larry D. Busboom, President
    510-463-8200   FAX 510-463-7492

Sunsweet Growers, Inc.
    901 N. Walton Ave., Yuba City 95993
    Mike Andrews, Vice President,
       Member Services
    916-674-5010

Tule River Cooperative Dryer, Inc.
    P.O. Box 4477, Woodville 93258
    16548 Road 168, Woodville 93257
    Mark Cartwright, Manager
    209-686-4685   FAX 209-686-8061

NUTS—ALMONDS

Bear River Almond Hulling Cooperative, Inc.
    P.O. Box 788, Wheatland 95692
    William Gilbert, President
    916-633-2391   FAX 916-633-2391

Blue Diamond Growers
    P.O. Box 1768, Sacramento 95812
    Walter F. Payne, President
    916-442-0771   FAX 916-446-8620

Butte County Almond Hull Association
    P.O. Box 417, Durham 95938
    John Crowe, Manager
    916-345-9404

California Almond Growers Exchange
    (See Blue Diamond Growers)

Central California Almond Growers Association
    10910 E. McKinley, Sanger 93657
    209-251-1050

Central Valley Almond Association, Inc.
    P.O. Box 428, McFarland 93250
    Stephen Taylor, Manager
    805-792-2171

Minturn Huller Cooperative, Inc.
    9080 South Minturn Road, P.O. Box 757
    Chowchilla 93610
    George Hughes, Manager
    209-665-1185

Northern Merced Hulling Association
    11076 North Santa Fe Drive, Ballico 95303
    Donald Harcksen, Manager
    209-667-2308   FAX 209-667-8945

North State Hulling Cooperative, Inc.
    P.O. Box 3522, Chico 95927
    Gary Pronsolino, Manager
    916-895-8686

Salida Hulling Association
    P.O. Box 1065, Salida 95368
    Levi Bowman, President
    209-545-0033

Westside Hulling Association
    P.O. Box 188, Westley 95387
    Anthony Plaza, Manager
    209-894-3921

NUTS—MACADAMIA

California Macadamia Society
    P.O. Box 1290, Fallbrook 92028-1290
    Jeannine T. Howell, Secretary/Treasurer
    619-743-0358

NUTS—PECANS

California Pecan Growers Association
    464 S. Mooney Blvd., Tulare 93274
    Carl Doyle, President
    209-686-2874   FAX 209-688-3542

NUTS—PISTACHIOS

California Pistachio Commission
    1915 N. Fine Ave., Fresno 93727
    Karen Dahlinger, President
    209-252-3345   FAX 209-252-2396

Western Pistachio Association
4924 W. Mineral King, Visalia 93291
Corky Anderson, Vice Chairman
209-734-0111

NUTS—WALNUTS

Diamond Walnut Growers, Inc.
P.O. Box 1727, Stockton 95201
William Cuff, President
209-467-6000

Golden State Walnut Growers Association
P.O. Box 3070, Modesto 95353
Walt Deardorff, President
209-521-1194

Mt. Konocti Growers, Inc.
P.O. Box 365, Kelseyville 95451
Richard A. Barnett, Manager
707-279-4213   FAX 707-279-2251

Sequoia Walnut Growers Association
P.O. Box 327, Visalia 93279
Jim Fesperman, Manager
209-734-3367   FAX 209-636-8917

Sun-Diamond Growers of California
P.O. Box 9024, Pleasanton 94566
Larry D. Busboom, President
510-463-8200   FAX 510-463-7492

Vegetables

Bonita Packing Company
P.O. Box 5079, Santa Maria 93456
Henri Ardantz, President
805-925-2478   FAX 805-928-5328

California Artichoke and Vegetable Growers Corp.
P.O. Box 1247, Castroville 95012
Edward Boutonnet, General Manager
408-633-2492   FAX 408-633-4363

California Corn Growers
P.O. Box 726, Chowchilla 93610
Paul Link, Manager
209-665-5775

California Mushroom Growers Cooperative Association
11300 Center Ave., Gilroy 95020
Frank Hinchberger/Dave Moore
408-683-2822   FAX 408-683-4192

California Sweet Potato Growers Association
5475 North Arena Way, Livingston 95334
Diane Oliveira, Manager
209-394-7935

California Tomato Growers Association, Inc.
P.O. Box 7398, Stockton 95267-0398
David L. Zollinger, President
209-478-1761   FAX 209-478-9460

California Tomato Research Institute, Inc.
2745 N. Hughes Ave., Ste. 105
Fresno 93705
Charles J. Rivara, Director
209-237-5884   FAX 209-237-5885

Castroville Artichoke People
P.O. Box 1247, Castroville 95012
Pat Hopper, President
408-633-2144

Central California Lettuce Producers Cooperative
512 Pajaro Street, Salinas 93901
Rusty Horton, Manager
408-758-2759   FAX 408-758-6972

Central California Tomato Growers Cooperative, Inc.
P.O. Box 696, Merced 95341
Timothy McCarthy, Manager
209-722-8086   FAX 209-383-2084

Cortez Growers Association, Inc.
12714 Cortez Avenue, Turlock 95380
Joe Kollmeyer, Manager
209-632-3118   FAX 209-632-2562

Diversified Producers Cooperative Association
P.O. Box 189, Shandon 93461
Lonnie Twisselman, President
805-238-5703

Fresh Produce Council
1601 E. Olympic Blvd., Ste. 212
Los Angeles 90021
Jan DeLyser, Exec. Vice President
213-629-4171   FAX 213-623-4035

Frozen Vegetable Council
1838 El Camino Real, Ste. 202
Burlingame 94010
Jean Bohannan, Secretary-Treasurer
415-697-6835   FAX 415-697-6646

Grower-Shipper Vegetable Association of Central California, Inc.
P.O. Box 828, Salinas 93902
H. Edwin Angstadt, President
408-422-8844   FAX 408-422-0868

Grower-Shipper Vegetable Association of Santa Barbara and San Luis Obispo Counties
P.O. Box 10, Guadalupe 93434
Richard Quandt, President
805-343-2215   FAX 805-343-6189

Half-Moon Bay Growers Association
845 Main Street, Half Moon Bay 94019
Dolores Mullin, Manager
415-726-4412

Imperial Valley Vegetable Growers Association
P.O. Box 358, El Centro 92244
444 S. Eighth St., Ste. B
El Centro 92243
Graydon Hall, Manager
619-353-1900   FAX 619-353-3550

International Sprout Growers Association
7946 Pocket Road, #18, Sacramento 95831
Ken Young, Manager
916-399-8644   FAX 916-399-1910

Livingston Farmers Association
P.O. Box 456, Livingston 95334
Tad Kurosaki, Chief Executive Officer
209-394-7941   FAX 209-394-1952

River Valley Marketing
P.O. Box 4460, Salinas 93912
Denny Bertelsman, Manager
408-755-1530   FAX 408-755-1514

Salinas Lettuce Farmers Co-op
P.O. Box 2176, Salinas 93902
Leland F. Rianda, General Manager
408-424-1666

South Bay Farmers Cooperative Association
567 Vista Lane, San Ysidro 92173
George Yamamoto, President
619-428-1656   FAX 619-428-8839

Sweet Potato Council of California
c/o Merced County Farm Bureau
646 South Los Banos Highway, Merced 95340
Mailing address: P.O. Box 366
Livingston 95334
209-723-3001

Tulelake Growers Association
P.O. Box 338, Tulelake 96134
Marshall Staunton, President
916-667-5214

Valley Growers and Packers
P.O. Box 299, Guadalupe 93434
805-343-2811

Western Growers Association
P.O. Box 2130, Newport Beach 92658
17620 Fitch Street, Irvine 92714
David L. Moore, President
714-863-1000   FAX 714-863-9028
1005-12th St., Ste. A, Sacramento 95814
916-446-1435   FAX 916-446-0181

FOREST AND
FOREST PRODUCTS

Associated California Loggers
555 Capitol Mall, Suite 745, Sacramento 95814
Ed Ehlers, Executive Director
916-441-7940   FAX 916-441-7942

Association of Consulting Foresters
8700 Greenback Lane, Ste. 1
Orangevale 95662
Scott Wall, Vice Chairman
916-989-9550   FAX 916-989-0798

California Christmas Tree Growers
1451 Danville Blvd., Ste. 102
Alamo 94507
Sharon M. Burke, Executive Director
510-837-7463   FAX 510-837-9588

Central Valley Section
3863 East Sussex, Fresno 93726
Ed Richard, Chairman
209-224-9807

Southern Section
5751 Casson Dr., Yorba Linda 92686
Mike Frederick/Rich DeRosa, Co-Chairman
714-993-0572

California Forestry Association
1311 I Street, Ste. 100
Sacramento 95814
William Dennison, President
916-444-6592

California Redwood Association
405 Enfrente Drive, Suite 200
Novato 94949
Christopher F. Grover, Executive Vice President
415-382-0662   FAX 415-382-8531

California Women in Timber
P.O. Box 7070, Eureka 95502-7070
707-444-2937

Forest Landowners of California
3807 Pasadena Ave., Ste. 100
Sacramento 95821
Thomas Kerr, Executive Director
916-972-0273

Redwood Region Conservation Council
589 Mendocino Ave., Room 6
Santa Rosa 95401
Phillip G. Lowell, Executive Vice President
707-578-7377

Redwood Region Logging Conference
P.O. Box 174, Garberville 95440
Charles Benbow, Secretary-Manager
707-923-3365   FAX 707-923-4009

Save-the-Redwoods League
114 Sansome St., Room 605
San Francisco 94104
John B. Dewitt, Executive Director
415-362-2352

FLORAL AND NURSERY

California Association of Nurserymen
4620 Northgate Blvd., Ste. 155
Sacramento 95834
Elaine Thompson, Executive Director
916-567-0200   FAX 916-567-0505

California Chrysanthemum Growers Association
788 San Antonia Road, Palo Alto 94303
Cap Utsunomiya, General Manager
415-494-1451   FAX 415-494-1452

California Floral Council
P.O. Box 1365, Davis, 95617-1365
Dr. Ray Hasek, Executive Vice President
916-753-7037   FAX 916-753-1693
5600 Avenida Encinas, Ste. 108
Carlsbad 92008
Marilu Johnson
619-431-2572

California Flower Cooperative
17098 El Rancho Way, Salinas 93907
P.O. Box 4819, Salinas 93912
Ray Yamagishi, Manager
408-758-5553

California Flower Market
640 Brannan Street, San Francisco 94107
David Ninomiya, President
415-392-7944   FAX 415-392-1298

California Protea Association
P.O. Box 2745, Vista 92085-2745
Herb Sulsky, Secretary
619-723-2751

California State Florists' Association
1610 Arden Way, Ste. 160, Sacramento 95815
C. Dennis Lewis, Executive Vice President
916-925-1232   FAX 916-925-0774

Monterey Bay Flower Growers
512 Pajaro St., Ste. 12
Salinas 93901
408-422-9063   FAX 408-422-9065

Monterey Greenhouse Company
384 Espinosa Road, Salinas 93907
John Stevenson, Manager
408-449-2412   FAX 408-449-0154

Nursery Growers Association of California
c/o Seatree Nurseries
P.O. Box 92, E. Irvine 92650
Tom Larson, President
714-651-9601

San Diego County Flower Growers Association
5600 Avenida Encinas, Ste. 100
Carlsbad 92008
Dave Pruitt, President
619-431-2572

San Francisco Flower Growers Association, Inc.
644 Brannan Street, San Francisco 94107
Leno Piazza, Jr., President
415-781-8410

Southern California Flower Growers, Inc.
755 Wall Street, Los Angeles 90014
Frank Kuwahara, President
213-627-2482   FAX 213-627-5065

SEEDS

Cal-West Seeds
P.O. Box 1428, Woodland 95695
Paul Baumer, Executive Vice President/
   General Manager
916-666-3331   FAX 916-666-5317

California Association of Nurserymen
4620 Northgate Blvd., Ste. 155
Sacramento 95834
Elaine Thompson, Executive Director
916-567-0200   FAX 916-567-0505

California Crop Improvement Association
Frank G. Parsons Seed Certification Center
University of California, Davis 95616
Robert Ball, Executive Secretary
916-752-0544   FAX 916-752-4735

California Seed Association
1715 Capitol Ave., Sacramento 95814
Richard Matteis, Executive Vice President
916-441-2251   FAX 916-446-1063

California Seed Council
c/o Department of Food and Agriculture
1220 N Street, Sacramento 95814
Robert Skaggs, Program Supervisor
916-322-4086

Dichondra Council
P.O. Box 1428, Woodland 95695
Edward D. Weimortz, President
916-666-3331   FAX 916-666-5317

Production Services
SUPPLIES AND SERVICES

California Ammonia Company
212 Frank West Circle, Ste. E
Stockton 95206
Paul Bennett, Chief Executive Officer
209-982-1000   FAX 209-983-0822

Dairymen's Feed and Supply Cooperative
323 E. Washington, Petaluma 94952
Andrew Moulyn, Manager
707-763-1585

Fruit Growers Supply Company
P.O. Box 7888, Van Nuys 91409
T.J. Lindgren, President
818-986-6480   FAX 818-783-1941

Mendocino County Farm Supply Company
303 Talmadge Road, Ukiah 95482
Jerry Fetzer, Manager
707-462-2603

Napa County Farm Supply
4081 Solano Avenue, Napa 94558
Stella Williams, Manager
707-224-0371

Placer Farm Supply
10120 Ophir Road, Newcastle 95658
Ron Berg, Manager
916-663-3748

San Luis Obispo County Farm Supply Company
675 Tank Farm Road, San Luis Obispo 93402
Jim Brabeck, General Manager
805-543-3751

San Mateo County Farm Supply Company
765 Main Street, Half Moon Bay 94019
Don Miramontes, Manager
415-726-4846

Stanislaus Farm Supply Company
624 East Service Road, Modesto 95351
Sam Bettencourt, Manager
209-538-7070
674 S. Hwy 59, Merced 95340
Marvin Dommer, Branch Manager
209-723-0704

Tehama County Farm Supply Company
712 Ash Street, Red Bluff 96080
Scott Moore, Manager
916-527-4151

Tri Valley Growers—Container Div.
41099 Boyce Road, Fremont 94538
Dick Dickson, Exec. Vice President
510-656-8800   FAX 510-656-7608

FARM CREDIT

Western Farm Credit Bank
3636 American River Drive, Sacramento 95864
P.O. Box 13106, 95813-4106
George D. Beitzel, President
916-485-6000   FAX 916-971-2837

Federal Land Bank Association of Bakersfield
Bakersfield Production Credit Association
5555 Business Park South
Bakersfield 93309
Box 9789, Bakersfield 93389
805-327-3234   FAX 805-327-1052

Central Coast Federal Land Bank Association, FLCA
Central Coast Production Credit Association
111 So. Mason, Arroyo Grande 93420
Box 1340, Arroyo Grande, 93421-1340
805-481-5900   FAX 805-473-2607

Central Valley Production Credit Association
800 W. Monte Vista Avenue
Box 2400, Turlock 95381
209-634-2960   FAX 209-634-9612

Federal Land Bank Association of Colusa
Colusa-Glenn Production Credit Association
310 Sixth Street, Box 449
Colusa 95932
916-458-4978   FAX 916-458-2614

Federal Land Bank Association of El Centro
Imperial-Yuma Production Credit Association
1415 State Street, El Centro 92243-2834
Box 1180, El Centro 92244-1180
619-352-5112   FAX 619-352-5235

Fresno-Madera Federal Land Bank Association
1240 West Olive Avenue, Fresno 93728
209-441-7894   FAX 209-486-7258

Fresno-Madera Production Credit Association
1250 West Olive Avenue, Fresno 93728
Box 9337, Fresno 93791
209-233-2091   FAX 209-233-7131

Intermountain Federal Land Bank Association
Sierra-Nevada Production Credit Association
255 West Peckham Lane, Reno, NV 89509
Box 20727, Reno, NV 89515-0727
702-825-7282   FAX 702-825-7598

Federal Land Bank Association of Kingsburg, FLCA
1580 Ellis Street
Box 6, Kingsburg 93631
209-897-5814   FAX 209-897-7943

North Coast Farm Credit Services, ACA
8741 Brooks Road, Box 929
Windsor 95492
707-838-4866   FAX 707-838-3456

Federal Land Bank Association of Northern California
Northern California Production Credit Association
130 Independence Circle, Philadelphia Square
Box 929, Chico 95927
916-895-8698   FAX 916-893-5314

Pacific Coast Federal Land Bank Association, FLCA
Pacific Coast Production Credit Association
921 Blanco Circle, Salinas 93901
Box 80021, Salinas 93912-0021
408-758-9815   FAX 408-422-6599

Sacramento Valley Federal Land Bank Association
Sacramento Valley Production Credit Association
283 Main Street, Box 269, Woodland 95695
916-666-3333   FAX 916-662-9034

Sierra-Bay Federal Land Bank Association
Sierra-Bay Production Credit Association
3984 Cherokee Road, Stockton 95215
Box 8070, Stockton 95208
209-931-3770   FAX 209-931-3855

Farm Credit Services of Southern California, ACA
4130 Hallmark Parkway
San Bernardino 92407
Box 6650, San Bernardino 92412
714-887-7018   FAX 714-887-8904

Federal Land Bank Association of Visalia
Visalia Production Credit Association
3010-A West Main St., Visalia 93291
Box 631, Visalia 93279
209-627-5050   FAX 209-627-4728

Federal Land Bank Association of Yosemite, FLCA
800 W. Monte Vista Ave.,
Box 3278, Turlock 95381
209-667-2366   FAX 209-634-9612

FARM LABOR

Agricultural Employers Labor Report
(Calif. Chamber of Commerce)
P.O. Box 1736, Sacramento 95812
Kathy Mason, Manager Business Publications
916-444-6670   FAX 916-443-4730

Agricultural Producers
25060 West Avenue Stanford, Ste. 200
Valencia 91355-3446
Russell L. Williams, President
805-257-4900   FAX 805-295-0430

Ag Employers, Inc.
P.O. Box 801, Corona 91718
Irma S. Caspaneda, General Manager
714-737-5940

Buena Ventura Lemon
P.O. Box 4095, Saticoy 93004
Leon Bad, Manager
805-647-1195   FAX 805-647-8573

California Grower Foundation
1108 Adams Street, St. Helena 94574
Lee Henderson, General Manager
707-963-7191 or 707-544-9420

Central California Farmers Association, Inc.
P.O. Box 627, Dinuba 93618
Charles Hoiland, Executive Secretary
209-591-4860

F & P Growers Association
743 Sespe Place, Fillmore 93015
Tom Walter, President
805-524-3933

Farm Employers Labor Service
1601 Expoisition Blvd., Sacramento 95815
George Daniels, General Manager
916-924-4124   FAX 916-923-5318

**Grower-Shipper Vegetable Association
of Central California, Inc.**
P.O. Box 828, Salinas 93902
H. Edwin Angstadt, President
408-422-8844   FAX 408-422-0868

**Grower-Shipper Vegetable Association
of Santa Barbara and San Luis Obispo Counties**
P.O. Box 10, Guadalupe 93434
Richard Quandt, President
805-343-2215   FAX 805-343-6189

Growers Farm Labor Association
P.O. Box 1568, Salinas 93902
H. Edwin Angstadt, President
408-422-8847

Growers Harvesting Committee
P.O. Box 745, Modesto 95353
Lee Tarkington-Lundrigan, Attorney-Manager
209-527-4404

Independent Growers Association, Inc.
P.O. Box 519, Greenfield 93927
408-674-5547

Los Padres Growers Foundation
P.O. Box 663, Santa Maria 93456
Birtice E. Card, President
805-934-7034

Nisei Farmers League
5108 East Clinton Way, Suite 115
Fresno 93727
Harry Kubo, President
209-251-8468

San Joaquin Farm Production Association
1225 East 1st Street, Stockton 95206
Bill Duarte, Manager
209-465-3423

Sequoia Growers Foundation
P.O. Box 551, 135 E. Front, Farmersville 93223
Scott Spear, President
209-747-3021

Southern California Growers Foundation
206 Railroad Blvd., Calexico 92231
James Legakes, President
Chuck Hewett, General Manager
619-357-7243   FAX 619-357-7281

Vegetable Bargaining Association of California
P.O. Box 519, Greenfield 93927
408-674-5547

Ventura County Citrus Growers Committee
5156 McGrath Street, Ventura 93003
Ray Mera, Manager; John Broome, President
and Chairman of the Board
805-656-6747

WATER—GENERAL

Association of California Water Agencies
910 K St., Suite 250, Sacramento 95814-3577
John P. Fraser, Exec. Director &
General Counsel
916-441-4545   FAX 916-441-7893

California Central Valley Flood Control Assoc.
921 11th Street (Elks Bldg. 703)
Sacramento 95814
916-446-0197

California Farm Water Coalition
423 W. Fallbrook, Ste. 201
Fresno 93711
Steve Hall, Executive Director
209-439-9663   FAX 209-439-3761

California Groundwater Association
P.O. Box 14369, Santa Rosa 95402-6369
Mike Martinson, Executive Director
707-578-4408   FAX 707-546-4906

California Mutual Water Companies Association
101 East Olive Avenue, Redlands 92373
Eugene P. McMeans, President
714-793-4901

California Water Resources Association
1127 - 11th St., Ste. 602, Sacramento 95814
Lou Smallwood, Executive Director
916-446-6507   FAX 916-446-1213

Central Valley Project Water Assoc.
1715 Capitol Ave., Sacramento 95814
Jason Peltier, Manager
916-448-1638   FAX 916-446-1063

Colorado River Association
770 Fairmont Ave., Ste. 100
Glendale 91203-1035
Gerald R. Zimmerman, Executive Director
818-543-4676

Sacramento Valley Landowners Association
2858 Illinois, Corning 96021
John Repanich
916-824-2752

State Water Contractors
555 Capitol Mall, Ste. 725
Sacramento 95814
George Baumli, General Manager
916-447-7357   FAX 916-447-2735

Water Association of Kern County
2724 L Street, Bakersfield 93301
Loron Hodge, Manager
805-324-8440

Water Education Foundation
717 K St., Ste. 517, Sacramento 95814
Robert M. Hagan, Ph.D., President
916-444-6240   FAX 916-448-7699

WateRuse Association of California
925 L Street, Ste. 1000
Sacramento 95814-3701
William R. Mills, Jr., President
916-442-8888   FAX 916-442-0382

WATER—AGENCIES ACTIVE IN IRRIGATION

Alpaugh Irrigation District
P.O. Box 129, Alpaugh 93201
Lavon Penrod, Manager
209-949-8323

Alta Irrigation District
P.O. Box 715, Dinuba 93618
Chris M. Kapheim, Manager
209-591-0800   FAX 209-591-5190

Anderson-Cottonwood Irrigation District
2810 Silver St., Anderson 96007-4297
Albert L. Davis, Manager-Secretary
916-365-7329

Antelope Valley-East Kern Water Agency
P.O. Box 3176, Quartz Hill 93586-0176
Wallace G. Spinarski, General Manager
805-943-3201   FAX 805-943-3204

Arvin-Edison Water Storage District
P.O. Box 175, Arvin 93203
C.E. Trotter, Manager
805-854-5573   FAX 805-854-5213

Banta Carbona Irrigation District
P.O. Box 299, Tracy 95378
Andrew W. Farrar, General Manager
209-835-4670   FAX 209-835-2009

Bard Water District
1473 Ross Rd., Winterhaven 92283
Ron Derma, Manager
619-572-0704

Belridge Water Storage District
P.O. Box 1087, Bakersfield 93302-1087
Robert E. Price, Manager
805-762-7316

Berrenda Mesa Water District
2100 F St., Ste. 100, Bakersfield 93301
H. Ronald Lampson, Manager
805-325-1284   FAX 805-325-5642

Biggs-West Gridley Water District
1713 W. Biggs Gridley Rd., Gridley 95948
Michael H. McLean, Manager
916-846-3317

Broadview Water District
P.O. Box 95, Firebaugh 93622-9542
David Cone, Manager
209-659-2004   FAX 209-659-3526

Buena Vista Water Storage District
P.O. Box 756, Buttonwillow 93206
Martin N. Milobar, Manager
805-324-4101   FAX 805-764-5053

Butte Water District
735 Virginia St., Gridley 95948
Lester Breeding, Secretary/Manager
916-846-3100

Byron Bethany Irrigation District
P.O. Box 273, Byron 94514
Fred K. Specht, Manager
510-634-3534   FAX 510-516-1239

Camp Far West Irrigation District
P.O. Box 308, Wheatland 95692
John Eachus, President
916-633-2847   FAX 916-633-9044

Carpenter Irrigation District
P.O. Box 2517, Orange 92669
Warren K. Hillebrecht, Manager
714-538-5032   FAX 714-730-8902

Cawelo Water District
17207 Industrial Farm Rd., Bakersfield 93308-9801
John L. Jones, Manager
805-393-0672   FAX 805-393-6073

Central California Irrigation District
P.O. Box 1231, Los Banos 93635
Michael Porter, Manager
209-826-1421   FAX 209-826-3184

Central San Joaquin Water Conservation District
311 E. Main St., Ste. 202, Stockton 95202
Grant Thompson, President
209-941-8714

Chowchilla Water District
P.O. Box 905, Chowchilla 93610
Barry J. Beal, Manager
209-665-3747   FAX 209-665-3740

Chualar County Water District
P.O. Box 436, Chualar 93925
Russ Hatch, Manager
408-679-2007

Coachella Valley
P.O. Box 1058, Coachella 92236
Thomas E. Levy, Manager
619-398-2651   FAX 619-398-3711

Colusa County Water District
P.O. Box 337, Arbuckle 95912
Lee Emrick, Manager-Secretary
916-476-2669

Consolidated Irrigation District
P.O. Box 209, Selma 93662
Eugene J. Branch, Manager
209-896-1661   FAX 209-896-8488

Contra Costa Water District
P.O. Box H20, Concord 94524-2099
William Seegmiller, General Manager
510-674-8000   FAX 510-674-8122

Corcoran Irrigation District
P.O. Box 566, Corcoran 93212
Thomas L. Vernon, Manager
209-992-5165

Cordua Irrigation District
P.O. Box 110, Marysville 95901
Charles J. Schnoor, Secretary
916-742-5157

Corning Water District
P.O. Box 738, Corning 96021
Winifred Jones, Manager
916-824-2914   FAX 916-824-3899

Cottonwood Water District
P.O. Box 576, Cottonwood 96022
Dennis Savage, Manager
916-347-3472

Delano-Earlimart Irrigation District
Rt. 1, Box 960, Delano 93215
Dale R. Brogan, Manager
805-725-2526   FAX 805-725-2556

Devil's Den Water District
23560 Lyons Ave., Ste. 220
Santa Clarita, 91321
Frank Sherrill, Manager
209-225-2866   FAX 209-225-6128

Dudley Ridge Water District
3636 N. First St., Ste. 123, Fresno 93726
James R. Provost, Manager
209-226-2920   FAX 209-226-3412

Dunnigan Water District
P.O. Box 84, Dunnigan 95937
Cynthia C. Peterson, Manager-Secretary
916-724-3271

East Contra Costa Irrigation District
P.O. Box 696, Brentwood 94513
Ross Rogers, Manager
510-634-3544

East Niles Community Services District
P.O. Box 6038, Bakersfield 93386
R.W. Stephens, Manager-Secretary
805-871-2011   FAX 805-871-2356

Eastern Municipal Water District
P.O. Box 8300, San Jacinto 92383-1300
J. Andrew Schlange, Manager
714-925-7676   FAX 714-929-0257

El Dorado Irrigation District
2890 Mosquito Rd., Placerville 95667
Willliam Robert Alcott, Manager
916-622-4513   FAX 916-622-1195

El Nido Irrigation District
P.O. Box 64, El Nido 95317
Jim Gudgel, Manager
209-722-6450

El Toro Water District
P.O. Box 4000, Laguna Hills 92654
Harlan G. Schroth, Manager
714-837-7050   FAX 714-837-7092

Empire West Side Irrigation District
P.O. Box 66, Stratford 93266
Ronnie Silva, Manager
209-947-3027

Fallbrook Public Utilities District
P.O. Box 1390, Fallbrook 92028-0900
Gordon W. Tinker, Manager
619-728-1125   FAX 619-728-6029

Feather Water District
280 Wilkie Ave., Yuba City 95991
Francis K. Silva, Manager
916-674-2120

Firebaugh Canal Water District
P.O. Box 97, Mendota 93640
Steve Chedester, Manager
209-655-4761   FAX 209-655-3658

Free Water County Water District
17504 E. Trimmer Springs, Sanger 93657
Sheldon Yost, President
209-787-2332

Fresno Irrigation District
1568 N. Millbrook Ave., Fresno 93703
Robert E. Leake Jr., Manager
209-233-7161   FAX 209-233-8227

Friant Water Users Authority
854 N. Harvard Ave., Lindsay 93247
Richard M. Moss, Manager
209-562-6305   FAX 209-562-3496

Georgetown Divide Public Utilities District
P.O. Box 4240, Georgetown 95634
Charles F. Gierau, Manager
916-333-4356   FAX 916-333-9442

Glenn-Colusa Irrigation District
P.O. Box 150, Willows 95988
Robert D. Clark, Manager
916-934-8881   FAX 916-934-3287

Glide Water District
P.O. Box 1054, Willows 95988-0001
Michael A. Alves, Manager
916-934-5476   FAX 916-934-7926

Goleta Water District
P.O. Box 788, Goleta 93116
Robert A. Paul, Manager
805-964-6761   FAX 805-964-7002

Grassland Water District
610 W. Pacheco Blvd., Los Banos 93635
Don Marciochi, Manager
209-826-5188   FAX 209-826-4984

Imperial Irrigation District
1284 Main St., El Centro 92243
Imperial 92251-0937
Charles L. Shreves, Manager
619-339-9477   FAX 619-339-9392

Irvine Ranch Water District
P.O. Box 6025, Irvine 92716-6015
Ronald E. Young, General Manager
714-476-7500   FAX 714-252-8525

Ivahoe Irrigation District
33777 Road 164, Visalia 93291
Ernest Veenstra, Manager-Secretary
209-798-1118   FAX 209-798-2479

Ivanhoe Public Utilities District
P.O. Box A, Ivanhoe 93235
Gordon G. Ponder, Manager
209-798-0512

James Irrigation District
P.O. Box 757, San Joaquin 93660-0757
John Mallyon, Manager
209-693-4356   FAX 209-693-4357

Kanawha Water District
P.O. Box 1054, Willows 95988-0001
Michael A. Alves, Manager
916-934-5476   FAX 916-934-7926

Kaweah Delta Water Conservation District
P.O. Box 1247, Visalia 93279-1247
James Crook, Manager
209-732-0111   FAX 209-732-7347

Kern County Water Agency
P.O. Box 58, Bakersfield 93302-0058
Thomas N. Clark, Manager
805-393-6200   FAX 805-395-1713

Kern Delta Water District
P.O. Box 49216, Del Kern Station
Bakersfield 93382
Gilbert H. Castle Jr., Manager
805-834-4656   FAX 805-836-1705

Kern-Tulare Water District
1820 21st St., Bakersfield 93301
C.W. Bowers, Manager
805-327-3132

Kings County Water District
200 N. Campus Dr., Hanford 93230
Cheryl Lehn, Manager
209-584-6412   FAX 209-584-6882

Kings River Conservation District
4886 E. Jensen Ave., Fresno 93725-1899
Jeff L. Taylor, Manager
209-237-5567   FAX 209-237-5560

Kings River Water District
15142 E. Goodfellow Ave., Sanger 93657
Allan R. Phillips, Manager
209-875-7721

LaCanada Irrigation District
P.O. Box 39, LaCanada, 91012-0039
Douglas M. Caister, Manager
818-790-6749

Laguna Irrigation District
5065—19½ Avenue, Riverdale 93656
Doug Rayner, Manager
209-923-4239

Lake Hemet Municipal Water District
P.O. Box 5038, Hemet 92344
Leonard C. Hale, Manager
714-658-3241   FAX 714-766-7031

Lakeside Irrigation Water District
9304 Houston Ave., Hanford 93230
Kenneth Cartwright, Manager
209-584-3396

Laton Community Services District
P.O. Box 447, Laton 93242-0447
Manuel Aguiar, President-Manager
209-923-4802

Le Grand-Athlone Water District
9158 S. Minturn Rd., Chowchilla 93610
David Serrano, President
209-665-4802

Lindmore Irrigation District
P.O. Box 908, Lindsay 93247-0908
Robert Baranek, Manager
209-562-2534

Lindsay-Strathmore Irrigation District
P.O. Box 846, Lindsay 93247-0846
Scott A. Edwards, Manager
209-562-2581   FAX 209-562-3882

Littlerock Creek Irrigation District
35141 N. 87th St. East, Littlerock 93543
Bradley J. Bones, Manager
805-944-2015   FAX 805-944-3668

Los Angeles Department of Water and Power
P.O. Box 111, Los Angeles 90051-0100
Daniel W. Waters, General Manager
213-481-4211

Lost Hills Water District
800 Chester Ave., Bakersfield 93308
Joe Steele, Manager
805-399-2185   FAX 805-399-4016

Lower San Joaquin Levee District
11704 W. Henry Miller Ave., Dos Palos 93620
Reggie N. Hill, Manager
209-387-4545   FAX 209-387-4237

Lower Tule River Irrigation District
P.O. Box 4388, Woodville 93258-4388
Roger W. Robb, Manager
209-686-4716   FAX 209-686-0151

Madera Irrigation District
12152 Rd. 28-1/4, Madera 93637-9106
Robert L. Stanfield, Manager
209-673-3514   FAX 209-673-0564

Malaga County Water District
3580 S. Frank St., Fresno 93725
Jerry Pearson, Manager
209-485-7353   FAX 209-485-7319

Mariposa County Water District
P.O. Box 784, Mariposa 95338-0784
Margie Williams, Secretary
209-966-2006   FAX 209-966-5147

Maxwell Irrigation District
P.O. Box 217, Maxwell 95955
Harold J. Myers, President
916-438-2773

Merced Irrigation District
P.O. Box 2288, Merced 95344-0288
Ross Rogers, Manager
209-722-5761   FAX 209-722-6421

**Metropolitan Water District of
Southern California**
P.O. Box 54133, Terminal Annex, Los Angeles 90054
Carl Boronkay, General Manager
213-250-6000   FAX 213-250-6950

Modesto Irrigation District
P.O. Box 4060, Modesto 95352
Joseph Marcotte Jr., Chief Executive Officer
209-526-7373   FAX 209-526-7573

Mojave Water Agency
P.O. Box 1089, Apple Valley 92307
Larry W. Rowe, General Manager
619-240-9201   FAX 619-240-2642

Montague Water Conservation District
P.O. Box 247, Montague 96064
Gregory P. Kuck, Manager
916-459-3371

Monterey County Water Resources Agency
P.O. Box 930, Salinas 93902
William F. Hurst, Manager
408-755-4860   FAX 408-424-7935

**Municipal Water District of
Orange County**
P.O. Box 15229, Santa Ana 92705-0229
Stanley E. Sprague, General Manager
714-973-1023   FAX 714-973-1707

Nevada Irrigation District
P.O. Box 1019, Grass Valley 95945-1019
James P. Chatigny, General Manager
916-273-6185   FAX 916-477-2646

North Delta Water Agency
921 11th St., Rm. 703, Sacramento 95814
Billy E. Martin, Manager
916-446-0197   FAX 916-446-2404

North Kern Water Storage District
P.O. Box 1195, Bakersfield 93302
Charles H. Williams, Manager
805-325-3116   FAX 805-325-7518

**North of the River
Municipal Water District**
P.O. Box 5577, Bakersfield 93388
Ralph L. Gifford, Manager
805-393-5411

**North San Joaquin
Water Conservation District**
111 W. Pine St., Lodi 95240
Conrad Weinzheimer Jr., Manager
209-333-1414

Oakdale Irrigation District
P.O. Box 188, Oakdale 95361-0188
Eugene O. Bergeron, Manager
209-847-0341   FAX 209-847-3468

Olcese Water District
P.O. Box 651, Bakersfield 93302
Donald L. Wahl, Manager
805-872-5563

Orange Cove Irrigation District
P.O. Box 308, Orange Cove 93646-0308
James C. Chandler, Manager
209-626-4461   FAX 209-626-4463

Orland-Artois Water District
P.O. Box 218, Orland 95963
August Lohse, Manager-Secretary
916-865-4304

Oroville-Wyandotte Irrigation District
P.O. Box 581, Oroville 95965-0581
Fritz Steppat, Manager
916-533-4578   FAX 916-533-9700

Pacheco Water District
P.O. Box 1447, Los Banos 93635
David Dermer, Manager
209-364-6392

Palo Verde Irrigation District
180 W. 14th Ave., Blythe 92225
Gerald M. Davisson, Manager
619-922-3144   FAX 619-922-8294

Panoche Water District
52027 W. Althea, Firebaugh 93622
Dennis Falaschi, Manager
209-364-6136   FAX 209-364-6122

Paradise Irrigation District
P.O. Box 128, Paradise 95967-0128
C. Phillip Kelly, Jr., Manager
916-877-4971

Patterson Water District
P.O. Box 685, Patterson 95363-0685
Glywn S. Chase III, Manager
209-892-6233

Pescadero Reclamation District 2058
3650 W. Canal, Tracy 95376
Tony Pimentel, Manager, President
209-835-2293

Pixley Irrigation District
P.O. Box 477, Pixley 93256-0477
Roger W. Robb, Manager
209-757-3545

Placer County Water Agency
P.O. Box 6570, Auburn 95604
Ed Schnabel, Manager
916-823-4850   FAX 916-823-4897

Plain View Water District
30215 S. Tracy Blvd., Tracy 95376
Mike Azpeitia, Manager
209-835-0375

Pleasant Valley County Water District
154 Las Posas Rd., Camarillo 93010-8570
LeRoy A. Miller, Manager
805-482-2119   FAX 805-484-5835

Pleasant Valley Water District
P.O. Box 468, Coalinga 93210
Joseph B. Summers, Manager
209-935-0282

Porterville Irrigation District
P.O. Box 1248, Porterville 93258
David L. Hoffman, Manager
209-784-0716

**Princeton-Codora-Glenn
Irrigation District**
   P.O. Box 98, Princeton 95970-0098
   Bernoy Bradford, Manager
   916-439-2248

Provident Irrigation District
   258 S. Butte St., Willows 95988
   Doug Davis, Manager
   916-934-4801

Rag Gulch Water District
   1820 21st St., Bakersfield 93301
   C.W. Bowers, Jr., General Manager
   805-327-3132

Rainbow Municipal Water District
   4555 Highway 76, Fallbrook 92028-9372
   Sammie E. Garcia, Acting Manager
   619-728-1178   FAX 619-728-2575

Raisin City Water District
   P.O. Box 174, Raisin City 93652
   Nancy Schwabenland, Secretary
   209-264-8348

Ramirez Water District
   P.O. Box 124, Marysville 95901
   Jim Rock, Manager
   916-531-6991

Reclamation District 108
   P.O. Box 50, Grimes 95950
   Tim Leather, Manager
   916-437-2221   FAX 916-437-2248

Reclamation District 307
   54084 S. River Road, Clarksburg 95612
   John Martinelli, President
   916-665-1655

Reclamation District 744
   P.O. Box 517, Clarksburg 95612
   Russell van Loben Sels, President
   916-665-1409

Reclamation District 900
   P.O. Box 673, West Sacramento 95691
   Kenneth Ruzich, Manager
   916-371-1483

Reclamation District 999
   38563 Netherlands Road, Clarksburg 95612-5003
   Richard E. Marshall, Manager
   916-775-2144

Reclamation District 1004
   134 5th St., Colusa 95932
   Gary D. Bailey, Manager
   916-458-7459

Reclamation District 1500
   P.O. Box 96, Robbins 95676
   Max S. Sakato, General Manager
   916-738-4423

Reclamation District 2047
   P.O. Box 150, Willows 95988
   Charles H. Michael, President
   916-934-8881   FAX 916-934-3287

Reclamation District 2068
   7178 Yolano Rd., Dixon 95620
   T.M. Hardesty, Manager
   916-678-5412   FAX 916-678-5414

Richvale Irrigation District
   P.O. Box 147, Richvale 95974
   Troy W. Kellett, Manager
   916-882-4243   FAX 916-882-4580

Riverdale Irrigation District
   P.O. Box 683, Riverdale 93656
   Frank J. Thomas, Manager
   209-867-3123

Rosedale-Rio Brave Water Storage District
   P.O. Box 867, Bakersfield 93302-0867
   Mary E. Collup, Manager
   805-589-6045

San Benito County Water District
   P.O. Box 899, Hollister 95024-0899
   David M. Porteur, President
   408-637-8218   FAX 408-637-7267

San Diego County Water Authority
   3211 Fifth Avenue, San Diego 92103
   Lester A. Snow, General Manager
   619-297-3218   FAX 619-297-9511

San Dieguito Water District
   59 East D St., Encinitas, 92024
   Warren Shafner, Manager
   619-753-1145   FAX 619-436-3592

**San Francisco Hetch Hetchy
Water & Power Dept.**
   1155 Market Street, 4th Floor
   San Francisco 94103
   Anson B. Moran, General Manager
   415-544-0725

San Luis Water District
   P.O. Box 2135, Los Banos 83635
   Daniel Nelson, General Manager
   209-826-4043   FAX 209-826-0524

Santa Clara County Water District
   5750 Almaden Expressway, San Jose 95118-3616
   Ronald R. Esau, General Manager
   408-265-2600   FAX 408-266-0271

Santa Fe Irrigation District
   P.O. Box 409, Ranch Santa Fe 92067-0409
   James Tolley, Manager
   619-756-2424   FAX 619-756-0450

Santa Maria Valley Water Conservation District
P.O. Box 364, Santa Maria 93456
James R. Sharer, President
805-925-5212

Santa Ynez River Water Conservation District
P.O. Box 157, Santa Ynez 93460-0157
Thomas M. Petersen, Manager
805-688-6015   FAX 805-688-3078

Saucelito Irrigation District
20712 Ave. 120, Porterville 93257
James A. Akins, Secretary/Manager
209-784-1208   FAX 209-784-3116

Semitropic Water Storage District
P.O. Box Z, Wasco 93280-0877
Wilmar Boschman, Manager
805-758-5113 or 327-7144
FAX 805-758-3219

Serrano Irrigation District
18021 E. Lincoln St., Villa Park 92667-6499
David H. Noyes, Manager
714-538-0079   FAX 714-538-5279

Shafter-Wasco Irrigation District
P.O. Box 158, Wasco 93280-0158
Harvey Williams, Manager
805-758-5153   FAX 805-758-6167

Solano Irrigation District
508 Elmire Rd., Vacaville 95687
Brice Bledsoe, Manager
707-448-6847   FAX 707-448-7347

South Montebello Irrigation District
864 W. Washington Blvd.
Montebello 90640-6191
Thomas Sinclair, Manager
213-721-4735

South San Joaquin Irrigation District
11011 E. Hwy. 120, Manteca 95336-9750
Barrett Kehl, Manager
209-823-3101   FAX 209-823-8406

South Sutter Water District
2464 Pacific Ave., Trowbridge 95659
Robert L. Melton, Manager
916-656-2242

South Yuba Water District
3002 Forty Mile Rd., Marysville 95901
Mike Rue, President
916-743-9108   FAX 916-533-0917

Stockton East Water District
P.O. Box 5157, Stockton 95205-0157
Edward M. Steffani, Manager
209-948-0333   FAX 209-948-0423

Stone Corral Irrigation District
37656 Road 172, Visalia 93291
William D. West, Manager
209-734-1370 or 528-4408

Stratford Irrigation District
P.O. Box 465, Stratford 93266
Bob Baley, Manager
209-947-3373

Sutter Extension Water District
4525 Franklin Rd., Yuba City 95993-9316
Paul W. Russell, Manager
916-673-7138

Tea Pot Dome Water District
105 W. Tea Pot Dome Ave., Porterville 93257
Douglas Peltzer, President
209-784-8641

Tehachapi-Cummings County Water District
P.O. Box 326, Tehachapi 93581
Robert J. Jasper, Manager
805-822-5504   FAX 805-822-5122

Tehama-Colusa Canal Authority
P.O. Box 1025, Willows 95988
John Campbell, General Manager
916-934-2125   FAX 916-934-2355

Terra Bella Irrigation District
24790 Ave. 95, Terra Bella 93270
J.E. Boudreau, Manager
209-535-4414   FAX 209-535-5168

Tranquillity Irrigation District
P.O. Box 487, Tranquillity 93668
Sargeant J. Green, Manager
209-698-7225   FAX 209-698-5105

Tri-Valley Water District
15142 E. Goodfellow Ave., Sanger 93657
Charles Kryder, President
209-875-7721

Tulare Irrigation District
P.O. Box 1920, Tulare 93275
Gerald C. Hill, Jr., Manager
209-686-3425   FAX 209-686-3673

Tulare Lake Basin Water Storage District
1109 Whitley Ave., Corcoran 93212-2399
Brent L. Graham, Manager
209-992-4127   FAX 209-992-3891

Tulelake Irrigation District
P.O. Box 699, Tulelake 96134
Earl C. Danosky, Manager
916-667-2249

Turlock Irrigation District
P.O. Box 949, Turlock 95381-0310
Ernest Geddes, Manager
209-883-8300   FAX 209-632-8181

United Water Conservation District
P.O. Box 432, Santa Paula 93061
Frederick J. Gientke, Manager
805-525-4431   FAX 805-525-2661

Vista Irrigation District
202 W. Connecticut Ave., Vista 92083-3596
Thomas M. Wilson, Manager
619-724-8811   FAX 619-724-0856

W.H. Wilbur Reclamation District #825
P.O. Box 1236, Cocoran 93212
Don M. Steele, General Manager
209-992-5642   FAX 209-992-2424

West Side Irrigation District, The
P.O. Box 177, Tracy 95378-0177
Lynn G. Bedford, President
209-835-0503   FAX 209-835-0503

West Stanislaus Irrigation District
P.O. Box 37, Westley 95387
Eugene Carson, Manager
209-894-3091   FAX 209-894-3383

Western Canal Water District
P.O. Box 176, Richvale 95974-0176
Dee Swearingen, Manager
916-342-5038   FAX 916-342-8233

Western Municipal Water District
P.O. Box 5286, Riverside 92517-5286
Donald L. Harriger, Manager
714-780-4170   FAX 714-780-3837

Westlands Water District
P.O. Box 6056, Fresno 93703
Jerald R. Butchert, Manager
209-224-1523   FAX 209-224-1560

Westside Water District
Route 1, Box 230, Williams 95987
Mary C. Wells, Manager
916-473-2876   FAX 916-473-2877

Wheeler Ridge-Maricopa Water Storage District
P.O. Box 9429, Bakersfield 93389-9429
Arnold S. Rummelsburg, Manager
805-858-2281   FAX 805-858-2643

Woodbridge Irrigation District
18777 N. Lower Sacramento Rd.
Woodbridge 95258
Anders Christensen, Manager
209-369-6808

**Yolo County Flood Control &
Water Conservation District**
34274 State Hwy. 16, Woodland 95695
James F. Eagan, Manager
916-662-0265   FAX 916-662-4982

Yuba County Water Agency
1402 D St., Marysville 95901-4226
Donn Wilson, Administrator
916-741-6278   FAX 916-741-6541

RESOURCE CONSERVATION

**California Association of
Resource Conservation Districts**
3830 U Street, Sacramento 95817
Betty Harris, Exec. Director
916-739-6251   FAX 916-739-1537

Area 1
P.O. Box 303, Weaverville 96093
Jim Aven, Director
916-623-4659

Area II
Vacant

Area III
113 Presley Way #1, Grass Valley 95945
Chauncey Poston, Director
916-272-5030

Area IV
P.O. Box 591, Oregon House 95962
George Steiner, Director
916-692-1153

Area V
P.O. Box 174, Davenport 95017
Roberta Smith, Director
408-429-1068

Area VI
2243 Los Encinos Rd., Ojai 93023
Harold Parker, Director
805-649-9270

Area VII
P.O. Box 878, Thermal, CA 92274
Eddie Walker, Director
619-347-7658

Area VIII
1276 Loma Vista Way, Vista 92084
Morris Johnson, Director
619-727-0487

Area IX
21593 W. Sunset Ave., Los Banos 93635
Dan Ramos, Director
209-826-0852
805-589-4803

*The Association of California Water Agencies publishes
a member agency roster which is available for a charge
of $150.00 to non-members, $15.00 to members.*
Address: *ACWA, 910 K St., Ste. 250,
Sacramento 95814-3577, (916) 441-4545. (Directory
does not include FAX numbers).*

PART II

Marketing Orders, Commissions, and Related State and Federal Commodity Marketing Programs
FEDERAL ORDER PROGRAMS

Almonds in California
Almond Board of California
  4700 Roseville Rd., Ste. 102
  North Highlands 95660
  Peggy Blanco, Manager
  916-338-2225   FAX 916-338-1019

Asparagus in California
California Asparagus Commission
  4565 Quail Lakes Dr., Ste. A-1
  Stockton 95207
  209-474-7581   FAX 209-474-9105

Dates in California
California Date Administrative Committee
  P.O. Box 1736, Indio 92202-1736
  Anne Ezell, Manager
  619-347-4510

Grapes in California
**California Desert Grape
Administrative Committee**
  82-365 Hwy 111, Suite 108, Indio 92201
  Dorothy Morgan, Manager
  619-342-4385

Grapes, Table in California
California Table Grape Commission
  P.O. Box 5498, Fresno 93755
  Bruce J. Obbink, President
  209-224-4997   FAX 209-224-4756

Grapes, Tokay in San Joaquin County, California
Tokay Marketing Agreement
  48 E. Oak, Lodi 95240
  P.O. Box 877, Lodi 95241
  Marjorie Parkison, Manager Secretary
  209-368-0685   FAX 209-368-4309

Kiwis in California
Kiwifruit Administrative Committee
  1540 River Park Dr., Ste. 110
  Sacramento 95815
  Mark Houston, Manager
  916-929-5314   FAX 916-929-3740

Lemons in California and Arizona
Lemon Administrative Committee
  25129 The Old Road, Ste. 304, Newhall 91381
  David A. Beavers, Manager
  805-253-0495   FAX 805-253-2764

Nectarines, Peaches, Bartlett Pears and Plums in California
California Tree Fruit Agreement
  P.O. Box 255383, Sacramento 95865
  701 Fulton Ave., Sacramento 95825
  Jon Fields, Manager
  916-483-9261   FAX 916-483-9605

Olives in California
California Olive Committee
  1903 N. Fine, #102
  Fresno 93727
  David J. Daniels, Manager
  209-456-9096   FAX 209-456-9099

Oranges, Navel and Valencia in California and Arizona
**Navel Oranges in Arizona and part of California,
Valencia Oranges in Arizona and part of California
Orange Administrative Committee**
  25129 The Old Road, Ste. 300, Newhall 91381
  Billy J. Peightal, Manager
  805-255-1380   FAX 805-255-9506

Pears, Winter in California, Oregon and Washington

Winter Pear Control Committee
813 S.W. Alder, Ste. 601
Portland, OR 97205
Herb Diede, Manager
503-223-8139   FAX 503-294-1428

Potatoes in Northeast California and Parts of Oregon

Oregon-California Potato Marketing Committee
700 NE Multnomah, Ste. 460
Portland, OR 97232
William Wise, Administrator
503-238-7500   FAX 503-239-4763

Prunes in California

Prune Marketing Committee
5990 Stoneridge Dr., Ste. 101
P.O. Box 10157, Pleasanton 94588
Richard Peterson, Executive Director
510-734-0339   FAX 510-734-0525

Raisins in California

Raisin Administrative Committee
3445 North First St., Ste. 101, Fresno 93726
P.O. Box 231, Fresno 93708
Clyde E. Nef, Manager
209-225-0520   FAX 209-225-0652

Walnuts in California

California Walnut Commission
1540 River Park Dr., Ste. 101
Sacramento 95815
Turner Oyloe, Chief Executive Officer
Dennis A. Balint, Marketing Director
916-646-3807   FAX 916-923-2548

Walnut Marketing Board
1540 River Park Drive, Suite 101
Sacramento 95815
Turner Oyloe, Executive Director
Mark Villata, Associate Director
916-922-5888   FAX 916-923-2548

FEDERAL AGREEMENT PROGRAM

Peanuts in the United States

Quality Regulation of Domestically Produced Peanuts. Includes peanuts produced in California.

Peanut Administrative Committee
P.O. Box 18856, Lenox Square Station
Atlanta, GA 30326
William Yarborough, Manager
404-261-7800   FAX 404-365-8589

STATE PROGRAMS

Alfalfa

Alfalfa Seed Production Research Board
531-D North Alta Avenue, Dinuba 93618
Ms. Pat Honchell, Manager
209-591-4792   FAX 209-591-5744

Apricots

California Apricot Advisory Board
1280 Boulevard Way, Suite 107
Walnut Creek 94595
Gene Stokes, General Manager
510-937-3660   FAX 510-937-0118

Artichokes

Artichoke Advisory Board
P.O. Box 747
10719 Merritt St., Castroville 95012
Ms. Patty Boman, Manager
408-633-4411   FAX 408-633-0215

Avocados

California Avocado Commission
1251 E. Dyer Rd., Ste. 200
Santa Ana 92705
Mark Affleck, President
714-558-6761   FAX 714-641-7024

Beans

Dry Bean Advisory Board
531-D North Alta Avenue, Dinuba 93618
Jerry R. Munson, Manager
209-591-4866   FAX 209-591-5744

Cantaloupes

Cantaloupe Advisory Board
531-D N. Alta Avenue, Dinuba 93618
Jerry R. Munson, Manager
209-591-5715   FAX 209-591-5744

Carrots

California Fresh Carrot Advisory Board
531-D N. Alta Avenue, Dinuba, CA 93618
Jim Melban, Manager
209-591-5675   FAX 209-591-5744

Celery

California Celery Research Advisory Board
531-D North Alta Ave., Dinuba 93618
Mr. Dana Dickey, Manager
209-591-0434   FAX 209-591-5744

Citrus

Citrus Research Board
25129 The Old Road, Ste. 300, Newhall 91381
Billy J. Peightal, Manager
805-255-1380   FAX 805-255-9506

Eggs

California Egg Commission
1150 N. Mountain Ave., Suite 114
Upland 91786
Robert Pierre, President
714-981-4923   FAX 714-946-5563

Dried Figs

California Fig Advisory Board
3425 North First St., Ste. 109
Fresno 93726
P.O. Box 709, Fresno 93712
Ron Klamm, Manager
209-224-3447   FAX 209-224-3449

Flowers

California Cut Flower Commission
1110-11th Street, Suite 305
Sacramento 95814
Susan Reed, President
916-447-6410   FAX 916-447-2350

Grapes

California Table Grape Commission
P.O. Box 5498, Fresno 93755
Bruce J. Obbink, President
209-224-4997   FAX 209-224-4756

Iceberg Lettuce

California Iceberg Lettuce Commission
P.O. Box 3354, Monterey 93942
Wade Whitfield, President
408-375-8277   FAX 408-375-8593

Iceberg Lettuce Research Advisory Board
512 Pajaro Street, Salinas 93901
Edward A. Kurtz, Manager
408-443-3205   FAX 408-422-0868

Kiwi

California Kiwifruit Commission
1540 River Park Drive, Suite 110
Sacramento 95815
Mark Houston, President
916-929-5314   FAX 916-929-3740

Melons

Central Valley Watermelon Growers Association
13979 S. Hwy 99, Manteca 95336
George Perry, Manager
209-823-6753   FAX 209-239-9858

Melon Research Board
531-D N. Alta Ave., Dinuba 93618
Mr. Dana Dickey, Manager
209-591-0435   FAX 209-591-5744

Milk Products

California Milk Advisory Board
400 Oyster Point Blvd., Suite 214
South San Francisco 94080
Ralph Watts, Chief Executive Officer
415-871-6455   FAX 415-583-7328

California Manufacturing Milk Advisory Board
1213-13th St., Modesto 95354
Ralph Watts, Chief Executive Officer
209-521-1060   FAX 209-527-0144

Peaches

California Cling Peach Advisory Board
160 Spear St., Ste. 1330, San Francisco 94105
P.O. Box 7111, San Francisco 94120
Thomas P. Krugman, General Manager
415-541-0100   FAX 415-541-0296

Peppers

California Pepper Commission
531-D North Alta Ave., Dinuba 93618
Mr. Dana Dickey, Manager
209-591-3925   FAX 209-591-5744

Pistachios

California Pistachio Commission
1915 N. Fine Ave., Fresno 93727
Karen Dahlinger, President
209-252-3345   FAX 209-252-2396

Pistachio Producers of California
20282 Road 21, Madera 93637-0739
Rob Koessler, President
209-673-8097   FAX 209-674-3409

Potatoes

California Potato Research Advisory Board
531-D N. Alta Ave., Dinuba 93618
Jim Melban, Manager
209-591-0436   FAX 209-591-5744

Poultry

California Poultry Health Board
3117-A McHenry Ave., Modesto 95350
Bill Mattos, Executive Director
209-576-6355   FAX 209-576-6119

California Poultry Industry Federation
3117-A McHenry Avenue, Modesto 95350
Bill Mattos, Executive Director
209-576-6355   FAX 209-576-6119

Prunes

California Prune Board
5990 Stoneridge Dr., Ste. 101
P.O. Box 10157, Pleasanton 94588
Richard Peterson, Executive Director
510-734-0150   FAX 510-734-0525

Raisins

California Raisin Advisory Board
3445 N. First St., Ste. 101
P.O. Box 5335, Fresno 93755
Clyde E. Nef, Manager
209-224-7010   FAX 209-224-7016

Rice

California Rice Industry Association
701 University Ave., Ste. 205
Sacramento 95825-6708
John R. Roberts, Executive Director
916-929-3996   FAX 916-929-0732

California Rice Promotion Board
335 Teagarden St., Yuba City 95991
Melvin D. Androus, Manager
916-674-1227   FAX 916-671-4664

California Wild Rice Program
335 Teagarden St., Yuba City 95991
Melvin D. Androus, Manager
916 673-1927   FAX 916-671-4664

Rice Research Board
335 Teagarden St., Yuba City 95991
Melvin D. Androus, Manager
916-673-6247   FAX 916-671-4664

Strawberries

California Strawberry Advisory Board
P.O. Box 269, Watsonville 95077
Dave Riggs, President
408-724-1301   FAX 408-724-5973

Processing Strawberry Advisory Board
251 East Lake Avenue, Suite 8
Watsonville 95076
P.O. Box 929, Watsonville 95077
George Faxon, Manager
408-724 5454   FAX 408-724-0295

Tomatoes

California Tomato Board
2017 N. Gateway, Ste. 102, Fresno 93727
Ed Beckman, Manager
209-251-0628   FAX 209-251-0705

California Processing Tomato Advisory Board
P.O. Box 1285
3960 Industrial Blvd., Suite 100
W. Sacramento 95691
Tom Ramme, Manager
916-371-3470   FAX 916-371-3476

Wheat

California Wheat Commission
P.O. Box 2267, Woodland 95695
Robert Drynan, Executive Director
Peter Rooney, Chairman
916-661-1292   FAX 916-661-1332

Agricultural Producers Marketing Law

Pear Program Committee
P.O. Box 255383, Sacramento 95865
701 Fulton Avenue, Sacramento 95825
Jon Field, Manager
916-483-9261   FAX 916-483-9605

California Beef Council Law

California Beef Council
551 Foster City Blvd., Suite A
Foster City 94404
Jane Anderson, Executive Director
415-571-7100   FAX 415-571-1831

Dairy Council of California Law

Dairy Council of California
1101 National Drive, Suite B
Sacramento 95834
Peggy Biltz, Chief Executive Officer
916-920-7691   FAX 916-920-7524

PART III

State and Federal Government
Education, Research, Administration,

UNIVERSITY OF CALIFORNIA DIVISION OF AGRICULTURE AND NATURAL RESOURCES

Kenneth R. Farrell
Vice President, Agriculture &
Natural Resources. Director
Cooperative Extension and Agricultural
Experiment Station
300 Lakeside Dr., 6th Floor
University of California
Oakland 94612-3560
510-987-0060   FAX 510-451-2317

(Position under recruitment)
Associate Vice President, ANR Programs.
Associate Director, Cooperative
Extension and Agricultural Experiment Station
300 Lakeside Dr., 6th Floor
University of California
Oakland 94612-3560
510-987-0026   FAX 510-987-0672

John E. Kinsella
Dean, College of Agricultural
and Environmental Sciences: Director,
ANR-Programs
University of California
Davis 95616
916-752-1605   FAX 916-752-4789

Wilford R. Gardner
Dean, College of Natural Resources:
Director, ANR Programs
University of California
Berkeley 94720
510-642-7171   FAX 510-642-4612

Seymour D. Van Gundy
Dean, College of Natural and Agricultural
Sciences: Director, ANR Programs
University of California
Riverside 92521
714-787-3101   FAX 714-787-4190

Nicelma J. King
Director, ANR Programs, North Central Region
1333 Research Park Drive
University of California
Davis 95616
916-757-8615   FAX 916-757-8866

Terrell P. Salmon
Director, ANR Programs, Northern Region
University of California
Davis 95616
916-757-8623   FAX 916-757-8866

William R. Hambleton
Director, ANR Programs, South Central
Region, Kearney Agricultural Center
9240 South Riverbend Avenue
Parlier 93648
209-891-2566   FAX 209-891-2593

Allyn D. Smith
Director, ANR Programs, Southern Region
Cooperative Extension
University of California
Riverside 92521
714-787-3321   FAX 714-787-4675

UNIVERSITY OF CALIFORNIA AGRICULTURAL FIELD STATIONS

Orchard Park Drive
University of California, Davis 95616
Harold R. Myers, Director
916-752-0126

**Deciduous Fruit Field Station
(Santa Clara County)**
90 North Winchester Blvd., Santa Clara 95050
Glen Bettelyoun, Acting Superintendent
408-296-1672

**Hopland Field Station
(Mendocino County)**
4070 University Road, Hopland 95449
R.M. Timm, Superintendent
707-744-1424

**Imperial Valley Agricultural Center
(Imperial County)**
1004 East Holton Road, El Centro 92243
Charles Dunn, Center Director
619-352-0111

**Kearney Agricultural Center
(Fresno County)**
9240 South Riverbend Avenue, Parlier 93648
Frederick H. Swanson, Superintendent
209-646-2794

Lindcove Field Station
(Tulare County)
22963 Carson Ave., Exeter 93221
Louis Whitendale, Superintendent
209-592-2408

Sierra Foothill Range Field Station
(Yuba County)
P.O. Box 28, Browns Valley 95918
John M. Connor, Superintendent
916-639-2501

South Coast Field Station
(Orange County)
7601 Irvine Blvd., Irvine 92718
Bob Bevacqua, Superintendent
714-559-4050

Tulelake Field Station
(Siskiyou County)
P.O. Box 447, Tulelake 96134
Harry Carlson, Superintendent
916-667-5117

West Side Field Station
(Fresno County)
P.O. Box 158, Five Points 93624
Jimmie Ross, Superintendent
209-884-2411

UNIVERSITY OF CALIFORNIA SMALL FARM CENTER

University of California
Davis 95616
Claudia Myers, Associate Director
916-752-6690

CALIFORNIA STATE UNIVERSITIES

California State Polytechnic University,
San Luis Obispo
San Luis Obispo 93407
Lark P. Carter, Dean, School of Agriculture
805-546-2161

California State Polytechnic University, Pomona
3801 West Temple Avenue, Pomona 91768
Dr. Allen C. Christensen, Dean
School of Agriculture
714-869-2200

California State University, Chico
1st and Normal Streets, Chico 95929
Dr. Lucas Calpouzos, Dean
School of Agriculture
and Home Economics
916-895-5131

California State University, Fresno
Shaw and Cedar Avenues, Fresno 93740
Dr. C.M. Smallwood, Dean, School of
Agriculture and Home Economics
209-294-2061

COUNTY OFFICES COOPERATIVE EXTENSION SERVICE UNIVERSITY OF CALIFORNIA

(Farm, Home & Youth Advisors)

Alameda
224 West Winton Ave., Room 174
Hayward 94544-1298
510-881-6341   FAX 510-670-5231

Amador
108 Court St., Jackson 95642
209-223-6482

Butte
2279 Del Oro Avenue, Suite B, Oroville 95965
916-538-7201   FAX 916-538-7140

Calaveras
P.O. Box 837, 891 Mountain Ranch Road
San Andreas 95249
209-754-6477   FAX 209-754-6472

Colusa
P.O. Box 180, 100 Sunrise Blvd., Ste. E
Colusa 95932
916-458-2105   FAX 916-458-4625

Contra Costa
1700 Oak Park Blvd., Bldg. A-2
Pleasant Hill 94523
510-646-6540   FAX 510-646-6708

Del Norte—(See Humboldt)

El Dorado
311 Fair Lane, Placerville 95667
916-626-2468   FAX 916-626-4756

Fresno
1720 South Maple Avenue, Fresno 93702
209-488-3285   FAX 209-488-1975

Glenn
P.O. Box 697, Road 200 East, Orland 95963
916-865-4487   FAX 916-865-4761

Humboldt/Del Norte
Ag Center Bldg., 5630 S. Broadway
Eureka 95501-6998
707-445-7351   FAX 707-444-9334

Imperial
1050 E. Holton Road, Holtville 92250-9615
619-352-9474   FAX 619-352-0846

Inyo/Mono
207 W. South Street, Bishop 93514
619-873-7854   FAX 619-872-1610

Kern
1031 S. Mt. Vernon Ave.
Bakersfield 93307
805-861-2631   FAX 805-834-9359

Kings
680 N. Campus Drive, Hanford 93230
209-582-3211, ext. 2730/2732
FAX 209-582-5166

Lake
Agricultural Center, 883 Lakeport Blvd.
Lakeport 95453
707-263-2281   FAX 707-263-2399

Lassen
Memorial Building, Susanville 96130
916-257-8311, ext. 111 or 916-257-6363
FAX 916-257-6129

Los Angeles
2615 So. Grand Ave., Ste. 400
Los Angeles 90007
213-744-4851, 4864, 4866   FAX 213-745-7513

Madera
328 Madera Avenue, Madera 93637
209-675-7879   FAX 209-675-0639

Marin
1682 Novato Blvd., #150B, Navato 94947
415-499-6352

Mariposa
5009 Fairgrounds Rd., Mariposa 95338-9435
209-966-2417 or 5321   FAX 209-966-2056

Mendocino
Agricultural Ctr./Courthouse, 579 Low Gap Rd.
Ukiah 95482
707-463-4495   FAX 707-463-4477

Merced
2145 W. Wardrobe Ave., Merced 95340
209-385-7403   FAX 209-722-8856

Modoc
202 W. 4th Street, Alturas 96101
916-233-3939, Ext. 400   FAX 916-233-3840

Mono—(See Inyo/Mono)

Monterey
118 Wilgart Way, Salinas 93901
408-758-4637   FAX 408-758-3018

Napa
1436 Polk Street, Napa 94559-2597
707-253-4221   FAX 707-253-4434

Nevada—(See Placer/Nevada)

Orange
1000 South Harbor Blvd., Anaheim 92805
714-447-7150   FAX 714-774-1733

Placer—Nevada
DeWitt Center, 11477 "E" Avenue
Auburn 95603
916-823-4581   FAX 916-889-7397

Plumas—Sierra
Route 1, Box 230, (Fairgrounds) Quincy 95971
916-283-6270   FAX 916-283-4210

Riverside
21150 Box Springs Road, Moreno Valley 92387
714-683-6491   FAX 714-788-2615

Sacramento
4145 Branch Center Road, Sacramento 95827
916-366-2013   FAX 916-366-4133

San Benito
649-A San Benito Street, Hollister 95023
408-637-5346   FAX 408-637-7111

San Bernardino
777 East Rialto Avenue
San Bernardino 92415-0730
714-387-2171   FAX 714-387-3306

San Diego
5555 Overland Ave., San Diego 92123
619-694-2845   FAX 619-694-2849

San Francisco
P.O. Box 34066, South Hall, Cow Palace
Geneva & Santos Avenue, San Francisco 94134
415-586-4115

San Joaquin
420 South Wilson Way, Stockton 95205
209-468-2085   FAX 209-462-5181

San Luis Obispo
2156 Sierra Way, Suite C
San Luis Obispo 93401
805-549-5940   FAX 805-549-4316

San Mateo
P.O. Box 37, 625 Miramontes St., Ste. 200
Half Moon Bay 94019
415-726-9059   FAX 415-726-9267

Santa Barbara
5266-B Hollister Ave., Ste. 215
Santa Barbara 93111
805-681-5630

Santa Clara
2175 The Alameda, San Jose 95126
408-299-2635   FAX 408-246-7016

Santa Cruz
1432 Freedom Blvd., Watsonville 95076
408-425-2591

Sierra—(See Plumas/Sierra)

Shasta
3179 Bechelli Lane, Ste. 206
Redding 96002
916-224-4900

Siskiyou
1655 South Main Street, Yreka 96097
916-842-2711

Solano
2000 West Texas Street, Fairfield 94533-4498
707-421-6790   FAX 707-429-5532

Sonoma
2604 Ventura Ave., Rm. 100-P
Santa Rosa 95403-2894
707-527-2621   FAX 707-527-2623

Stanislaus
733 County Center III Court, Modesto 95355
209-525-6654

Sutter—Yuba
142-A Garden Highway, Yuba City 95991
916-741-7515   FAX 916-673-5368

Tehama
P.O. Box 370, 1754 Walnut Street
Red Bluff 96080
916-527-3101   FAX 916-527-3103 (call first)

Trinity
P.O. Box 490, Fairgrounds, Hayfork 96041
916-628-5495   FAX 916-628-5495

Tulare
County Civic Center, Ag Bldg.
Woodland & West Main, Visalia 93291
209-733-6363   FAX 209-733-6720

Tuolumne
2 South Green Street, Sonora 95370
209-533-5695   FAX 209-532-8978

Ventura
800 South Victoria Avenue, Ventura 93009
805-654-2924   FAX 805-654-2424

Yolo
70 Cottonwood Street, Woodland 95695
916-666-8143   FAX 916-666-8736

State of California
Department of Food and Agriculture
1220 N. Street, Sacramento, 95814
Public Information — 916-654-0462

EXECUTIVE OFFICE:
FAX 916-654-0403

Henry Voss, Director
916-654-0433

Robert L. Shuler, Chief Deputy Director
916-654-0321

A.J. Yates, Deputy Director
916-654-0309

Rebecca Davis, Assistant to the Director
916-654-1020

Howard R. Heritage, Legislative Coordinator
916-654-0326

Janice Strong, Legislative Assistant
916-654-1016

Herb Cohen, Administrative Advisor
916-654-1393

Robert Alderette, Equal Employment Officer
916-654-1005

Carl DeWing, Communications Officer
916-654-0462

Joe Bandy, Regional Coordinator
916-654-1373

John Donahue, Regional Coordinator
916-654-1373

DIVISION OF ADMINISTRATIVE SERVICES
FAX 916-654-0542

Shamim Khan, Assistant Director
916-654-1020

Financial Services
Elaine Berghausen, Chief
916-654-0306

Labor Relations
Sis Narramore, Labor Relations Officer
916-654-1019

Human Relations
Vacant, Chief
916-654-0304

Management Analysis
George Deese, Officer
916-654-0990

DIVISION OF ANIMAL INDUSTRY
FAX 916-654-0542

Patton L. Smith, D.V.M., Assistant Director
916-654-0881

Animal Health Branch
Vacant, Chief
916-654-1447

Livestock Identification Branch
Vacant, Chief
916-654-0889

Meat Inspection Branch
L.G. Billingsley, D.V.M., Chief
916-654-0504

Milk and Dairy Foods Control Branch
Richard Tate, Chief
916-654-0773

DIVISION OF FAIRS AND EXPOSITIONS
FAX 916-924-2710

Kim Myrman, Assistant Director
916-924-2226

Carol Chesbrough, Senior Legal Council
916-924-2115

Leon Vann, Engineering Manager
916-924-2057

Norm Towne, Director of Horse Racing
& Satellite Wagering
916-924-2232

Stan Wirth, Financial Officer
916-924-2227

DIVISION OF INSPECTION SERVICES
FAX 916-654-0876

Ezio Delfino, Assistant Director
916-654-0792

Chemistry Laboratory Services
Bill Cusick, Chief
916-427-4595

Feed, Fertilizer and Livestock Drugs
Steve Wong, Chief
916-654-0574

Fruit and Vegetable Quality Control
Fresh Products for Processing
John Wiley, Chief
916-654-0941

Shipping Point Inspection
Bob Wynn, Chief
916-654-0810

Standardization
Reginald Marcellino, Chief
916-654-0810

Egg Quality Control
Ardie Ferrill, Program Supervisor
916-654-0800

Grain and Commodity Inspection
David Edmiston, Chief
916-654-1429

DIVISION OF MARKETING SERVICES
FAX 916-654-1250

Jed Adams, Assistant Director
916-654-1240

Vacant, Special Assistant
916-654-1245

Agricultural Statistics Branch
H. James Tippett, Chief
916-654-0895

Market Enforcement Branch
George Reese, Chief
916-654-1237

Market News Branch
Art Verissimo, Chief
916-654-0298

Marketing Branch
Richard Gassman, Chief
916-654-1245
Direct Marketing
Lynn Horel, Senior Agricultural Economist
916-654-0824

Milk Pooling Branch
Glenn Gleason, Chief
916-654-0795

Milk Stabilization Branch
David Ikari, Chief
916-654-1456

DIVISION OF MEASUREMENT STANDARDS
FAX 916-366-5179

8500 Fruitridge Rd., Sacramento 95826

Darrell A. Guensler, Assistant Director
916-366-5119

Barbara Bloch, Special Assistant
916-366-5119

Metrology
Joseph Rothleder, Principal State Metrologist
916-366-5119

Quantity Control & Weighing and and Measuring Devices
Jim Tollefson, Chief
916-366-5119

Special Projects/Metrics
Mike Saling, Manager
916-366-5119

Weighmaster Enforcement & Petroleum Products
Manuel Gonzales, Chief
916-366-5119

DIVISION OF PLANT INDUSTRY
FAX 916-654-1018

Isi Siddiqui, Assistant Director
916-654-0317

Bill Callison, Special Assistant
916-654-1022

Analysis & Identification
Bob Roberson, Chief
916-654-1391

Control & Eradication
Len Foote, Chief
916-654-0768

Border Stations Pest Exclusion & Nursery
Martina Haleamau, Chief
916-653-1440

CALIFORNIA COUNTY AGRICULTURAL COMMISSIONERS

Alameda
224 West Winton Ave., Room 184
Hayward 94544
Michael A. Greene
415-670-5232   FAX 415-783-3928

Amador
Amador County Airport Building, Sutter Hill
108 Court St., Jackson 95642
David A. Thompson, Jr.
209-223-6481   FAX 209-223-3312

Butte
316 Nelson Avenue, P.O. Box 1229
Oroville 95965
Richard Price
916-538-7381   FAX 916-538-7594

Calaveras
Government Center, El Dorado Rd.
San Andreas 95249
Jearl Howard
209-754-6504   FAX 209-754-6521

Colusa
100 Sunrise Blvd., Ste. F, Colusa 95932
Harry Krug
916-458-5867   FAX 916-458-5000

Contra Costa
161 John Glenn Drive, Concord 94520
John H. de Fremery
510-646-5250   FAX 510-646-5732

Del Norte
2650 Washington Blvd., Crescent City 95531
Griffith Yamamoto
707-464-7231   FAX 707-464-7235

El Dorado
311 Fair Lane, Placerville 95667
Edio P. Delfino
916-621-5520   FAX 916-626-4756

Fresno
1730 South Maple Avenue, Fresno 93702
Cosmo C. Insalaco
209-488-3510   FAX 209-488-3679

Glenn
P.O. Box 351, 720 N. Colusa St.,
Willows 95988
Ed Romano
916-934-6501   FAX 916-934-6503

Humboldt
5630 S. Broadway, Eureka 95501
John Falkenstrom
707-445-7223   FAX 707-445-7224

Imperial
150 S. 9th St., El Centro 92243-2801
Stephen L. Birdsall
619-339-4314   FAX 619-353-9420

Inyo/Mono
County Services Building
207 W. South Street, Bishop 93514-3492
Donald R. Muse
619-873-7860   FAX 619-872-1610

Kern
1001 South Mt. Vernon Ave.
Bakersfield 93307
Ted Davis
805-861-2306   FAX 805-397-5097

Kings
680 N. Campus Drive, Ste. B, Hanford 93230
M. Hugh Handley
209-582-3211, ext. 2830
FAX 209-582-5251

Lake
883 Lakeport Boulevard, Lakeport 95453
Mark Lockhart
707-263-2271   FAX 707-263-1052

Lassen
175 Russell Avenue, Susanville 96130
Kenneth R. Smith
916-257-8311 ext. 110
FAX 916-257-6515

Los Angeles
3400 La Madera Ave., El Monte 91732
E. Leon Spaugy
818-575-5451   FAX 818-350-7077

Madera
332 Madera Avenue, Madera 93637
Donald O. Cripe
209-675-7876   FAX 209-674-4071

Marin
1682 Novato Blvd., Novato 94947
Jack Schrock
415-899-8601   FAX 415-899-8605

Mariposa
5009 Fairgrounds Road
P.O. Box 905, Mariposa 95338-0905
Donald O. Cripe
209-966-2075   FAX 209-966-2056

Mendocino
579 Low Gap Road, Ukiah 95482
David Bengston
707-463-4208
FAX 707-463-0240

Merced
2139 W. Wardrobe Ave., Merced 95340-6495
Michael J. Tanner
209-385-7431   FAX 209-385-7439

Modoc
202 West 4th Street, Alturas 96101-3915
Clinton "Bud" Greenbank
916-233-3939 ext. 401
FAX 916-233-5542

Monterey
120 Wilgart Way, Salinas 93901
Richard W. Nutter
408-758-3876   FAX 408-422-5003

Napa
1436 Polk Street, Napa 94559-2596
Stephen Bardessono
707-253-4357   FAX 707-253-4881

Nevada
255 South Auburn Street
Grass Valley 95945
Paul Boch
916-273-2648   FAX 916-273-1713

Orange
1010 South Harbor Blvd., Anaheim 92805-5597
James D. Harnett
714-447-7100   FAX 714-774-2741

Placer
11477 E Avenue, Auburn 95603-2799
John H. Wilson
916-889-7372   FAX 916-823-1698

Plumas/Sierra
208 Fairgrounds Rd., Quincy 95971
Frederick H. Surber
916-283-6365   FAX 916-283-4210

Riverside
4080 Lemon St., Room 19
P.O. Box 1089, Riverside 92501
James O. Wallace
714-275-3000   FAX 714-275-3012

Sacramento
4137 Branch Center Rd., Sacramento 95827
Frank E. Carl
916-366-2003   FAX 916-366-4150

San Benito
3220 Southside Rd., P.O. Box 699
Hollister 95023
Mark Tognazzini
408-637-5344   FAX 408-637-9015

San Bernardino
777 E. Rialto Ave., San Bernardino 92415-0720
Edouard P. Layaye
714-387-2115   FAX 714-387-2449

San Diego
5555 Overland Ave., Bldg. 3
San Diego 92123
Kathleen Thuner
619-694-2741   FAX 619-565-7046

San Francisco
501 Army St., Ste. 109-A
San Francisco 94124
G. Evan Weeth
415-285-5010   FAX 415-285-8776

San Joaquin
1868 East Hazelton Ave., P.O. Box 1809
Stockton 95201
Erwin B. Eby
209-468-3300   FAX 209-468-3330

San Luis Obispo
2156 Sierra Way, Ste A
San Luis Obispo 93401
Richard Greek
805-549-5910   FAX 805-546-1035

San Mateo
728 Heller St., P.O. Box 999
Redwood City 94064
George Ginilo
415-363-4700   FAX 415-367-0130

Santa Barbara
263 Camino Del Remedio
Santa Barbara 93110
Ronald Gilman
805-681-5600   FAX 805-681-5603

Santa Clara
1553 Berger Dr., Bldg. 1, San Jose 95112
Greg Van Wassenhove
408-299-2171   FAX 408-286-2460

Santa Cruz
175 Westridge Dr.., Watsonville 95076
David Moeller
408-761-4080   FAX 408-761-4082

Shasta
3179 Bechelli Lane, Ste. 210
Redding 96002
Kit Cassaday
916-224-4949   FAX 916-224-4951

Siskiyou
525 South Foothill Drive, Yreka 96097
Edmond W. Hale
916-842-8025   FAX 916-842-6690

Solano
2000 West Texas Street, Fairfield 94533
Susan Cohen
707-421-7465   FAX 707-429-0827

Sonoma
2604 Ventura Ave., Rm. 101
Santa Rosa 95403-2810
Eric Lauritzen
707-527-2371   FAX 707-527-3850

Stanislaus
725 County Center Three Court
Modesto 95355
Keith L. Mahan
209-525-4610   FAX 209-525-4619

Sutter
142 Garden Highway, Yuba City 95991
Stacy Carlsen
916-741-7500   FAX 916-741-7510

Tehama
1760 Walnut Street, P.O. Box 38
Red Bluff 96080
Heidi Walker-Hill
916-527-4504   FAX 916-529-1049

Trinity
Box 1466, Civil Defense Hall
Weaverville 96093
Mary Pfeifler
916-623-1356   FAX 916-623-1356

Tulare
Ag Bldg. - 2500 Burrel Ave., Visalia 93291-4584
Lenord Craft, Jr.
209-733-6391   FAX 209-625-0624

Tuolumne
2 South Green St., Sonora 95370
Gerald A. Benincasa
209-533-5691   FAX 209-533-5520

Ventura
815 Santa Barbara St., Agricultural Bldg.,
P.O. Box 889, Santa Paula 93060
W. Earl McPhail
805-933-3165   FAX 805-525-8922

Yolo
70 Cottonwood Street, Woodland 95695
Ray Perkins
916-666-8140   FAX 916-662-6094

Yuba
938 - 14th Street, Marysville 95901
Dempsey Engle
916-741-6484   FAX 916-743-4442

State Board of Food and Agriculture
Member and County

John Kautz, President..............................San Joaquin
Kenneth R. Farrell ....Alameda
William Borror ....Tehama
Allen Christensen...............................San Bernardino
Sig Christierson......................................Monterey
Richard Keehn.......................................Mendocino
Donald Daley, Jr. ....San Diego

George De Medeiros...Tulare
Robert Moore ....Los Angeles
Thomas DiMare ....Stanislaus
Dorothy Ann Harper.....................................Santa Clara
Louise Willey ....Imperial
Jacqueline Heather..Orange
Conception Minsky ....Los Angeles

Howard R. Heritage, Executive Officer ....Sacramento

CALIFORNIA COUNTY SEALERS OF WEIGHTS AND MEASURES

Alameda
333 5th St., Oakland 94607
Patrick E. Nichols
510-368-7343   FAX 510-444-3879

Amador
108 Court St., Jackson 95642
David A. Thompson, Jr.
209-223-6481   FAX 209-223-3312

Butte
316 Nelson Ave., P.O. Box 1229
Oroville 95965
Richard Price
916-538-7381   FAX 916-538-7594

Calaveras
County Govt. Center, El Dorado Rd.
San Andreas 95249
Jearl Howard
209-754-6504   FAX 209-754-6521

Colusa
100 Sunrise Blvd., Ste. F,
Colusa 95932
Harry Krug
916-458-5867   FAX 916-458-5000

Contra Costa
161 John Glenn Dr., Concord 94520
John H. deFremery
510-646-5250   FAX 510-646-5732

Del Norte
2650 Washington Blvd., Crescent City 95531
Griffith Yamamoto
707-464-7231   FAX 707-464-7235

El Dorado
311 Fair Lane, Placerville 95667
Edio P. Delfino
916-621-5520   FAX 916-626-4756

Fresno
1730 S. Maple Ave., Fresno 93702
Cosmo Insalaco
209-488-3510   FAX 209-488-3679

Glenn
720 N. Colusa St., P.O. Box 351
Willows 95988
Ed Romano
916-934-6501   FAX 916-934-6503

Humboldt
5630 S. Broadway, Eureka 95501
John Falkenstrom
707-445-7223   FAX 707-445-7224

Imperial
150 S. 9th St., El Centro 92243-2801
Stephen L. Birdsall
619-339-4314   FAX 619-353-9420

Inyo/Mono
207 W. South St., Bishop 93514-3492
Donald R. Muse
619-873-7860   FAX 619-872-1610

Kern
1116 E. California Ave., Bakersfield 93307
Monty Hopper
805-861-2418   FAX 805-324-0668

Kings
680 N. Campus Dr., Hanford 93230
M. Hugh Handley
209-582-3211 ext. 2830   FAX 209-582-5251

Lake
883 Lakeport Blvd., Lakeport 95453
Mark Lockhart
707-263-2271   FAX 707-263-1052

Lassen
175 Russell Avenue, Susanville 96130
Kenneth R. Smith
916-257-8311 ext. 110   FAX 916-257-6515

Los Angeles
3400 La Madera Ave.
El Monte 91732
E. Leon Spaugy
818-575-5451   FAX 818-350-7077

Madera
332 Madera Avenue, Madera 93637-5499
Donald O. Cripe
209-675-7876   FAX 209-674-4071

Marin
1682 Novato Blvd., Novato 94947
Jack Schrock
415-899-8601   FAX 415-899-8605

Mariposa
P.O. Box 905, 5009 Fairground Rd.
Mariposa 95338-0905
Donold O. Cripe
209-966-2075   FAX 209-966-2056

Mendocino
Courthouse, 579 Low Gap Road, Ukiah 95482
David Bengston
707-463-4208   FAX 707-463-0240

Merced
2139 W. Wardrobe Ave., Merced 95340-6495
Michael J. Tanner
209-385-7431   FAX 209-385-7439

Modoc
202 West 4th Street, Alturas 96101
Clinton "Bud" Greenbank
916-233-3939 ext. 401   FAX 916-233-5542

Monterey
120 Wilgart Way, Salinas 93901
Joseph L. Goodrick, Jr.
408-758-3876   FAX 408-422-5003

Napa
7292 Silverado Trail, Napa 94558
Ted Tamagni
707-944-8714   FAX 707-253-4881

Nevada
255 South Auburn Street, Grass Valley 95945-7289
Paul Boch
916-273-1049   FAX 916-273-1713

Orange
1010 South Harbor Blvd., Anaheim 92805
James D. Harnett
714-447-7100   FAX 714-774-2741

Placer
11477 E Avenue, Auburn 95603-2799
John H. Wilson
916-889-7372   FAX 916-823-1698

Plumas/Sierra
208 Fairgrounds Rd., Quincy 95971
Frederick H. Surber
916-283-6365   FAX 916-283-4120

Riverside
2950 Washington St., P.O. Box 1089
Riverside 92504
Dan Riley
714-275-3030   FAX 714-276-4728

Sacramento
4137 Branch Center Rd., Sacramento 95827
Frank E. Carl
916-366-2003   FAX 916-366-4150

San Benito
3220 Southside Rd., P.O. Box 699
Hollister 95023
Mark Tognazzini
408-637-5344   FAX 408-637-9015

San Bernardino
777 E. Rialto Ave., San Bernardino 92415
Gerald Hanson
714-387-2136   FAX 714-387-2143

San Diego
5555 Overland Ave., Bldg. 3
San Diego 92123
Kathleen A. Thuner
619-694-2741   FAX 619-565-7046

San Francisco
501 Army St., Ste. 109-A
San Francisco 94124
G. Evan Weeth
415-285-5010   FAX 415-285-8776

San Joaquin
1868 East Hazelton Ave., P.O. Box 1809
Stockton 95201
Erwin B. Eby
209-468-3300   FAX 209-468-3330

San Luis Obispo
2156 Sierra Way, Ste A
San Luis Obispo 93401
Richard Greek
805-549-5910   FAX 805-546-1035

San Mateo
728 Heller St., P.O. Box 999
Redwood City 94064
George Ginilo
415-363-4700   FAX 415-367-0130

Santa Barbara
263 Camino Del Remedio
Santa Barbara 93110
Ronald Gilman
805-681-5600   FAX 805-681-5603

Santa Clara
1553 Berger Dr., Bldg. 1, San Jose 95112
Greg Van Wassenhove
408-299-2712   FAX 408-286-2460

Santa Cruz
175 Westridge Dr., Watsonville 95076
David Moeller
408-761-4080   FAX 408-761-4082

Shasta
3179 Bechelli Lane, Ste. 210
Redding 96002
Kit Cassaday
916-224-4949   FAX 916-224-4951

Siskiyou
525 South Foothill Drive, Yreka 96097
Edmond W. Hale
916-842-8025   FAX 916-842-6690

Solano
2000 W. Texas St., Fairfield 94533
Susan Cohen
707-421-7465   FAX 707-429-0827

Sonoma
2604 Ventura Ave., Rm. 101
Santa Rosa 95401-2893
Eric Lauritzen
707-527-2371   FAX 707-527-3850

Stanislaus
725 County Center Three Court
Modesto 95355
Keith L. Mahan
209-525-4610   FAX 209-525-4619

Sutter
142 Garden Highway, Yuba City 95991
Stacy Carlsen
916-741-7500   FAX 916-741-7510

Tehama
1760 Walnut Street, P.O. Box 38
Red Bluff 96080
Heidi Walker-Hill
916-527-4504   FAX 916-529-1049

Trinity
Civil Defense Hall, Box 1466,
Weaverville 96093
Mary Pfeifler
916-623-1356   FAX 916-623-1356 (Manual Fax)

Tulare
Ag Bldg.-2500 Burrel Ave., Visalia 93291-4584
Lenord Craft, Jr.
209-733-6391   FAX 209-625-0624

Tuolumne
2 S. Green St., Sonora 95370
Gerald A. Benincasa
209-533-5691   FAX 209-533-5520

Ventura
800 S. Victoria Ave., Ventura 93009
William H. Korth
805-654-2444   FAX 805-648-9212

Yolo
70 Cottonwood Street, Woodland 95695
Ray Perkins
916-666-8140   FAX 916-662-6094

Yuba
938 - 14th Street, Marysville 95901
Dempsey Engle
916-741-6484   FAX 916-743-4442

California's Certified Farmers' Markets
Many markets are seasonal. Call for days and time of operation.

NORTHERN

Alameda County
Alameda
  Central Ave. between Webster & 6th
  510-798-7061

Berkeley
  Derby St. between Milvia &
  Martin Luther King Dr.
  510-548-2220

  Center St. at Martin
  Luther King, Jr. Way
  510-548-2220

Livermore
  2nd & K Sts.
  510-373-1795

Oakland
  Jack London Water Front
  510-798-7061

  Downtown, 9th St. & Broadway
  510-456-3276

Butte County
Chico
  Orient and E. 5th
  916-345-8569

City parking lot between E. 2nd
and Wall
916-345-8569

Oroville
Myers & Bird Sts., downtown
916-534-6216

Colusa County
Arbuckle
5th & Eddy, downtown
916-476-2170

Colusa
4th & Market, parking lot
across from post office
916-458-5355

Contra Costa County
Danville
"Old Town"-Railroad Ave.
parking lot
510-798-7061

Pleasant Hill
Hill Crest Center
Taylor & Morello
510-706-1362

Richmond
Richmond Civic Center
In front of library
510-724-2283

Walnut Creek
Broadway & Lincoln
Library parking lot
510-706-1362

El Dorado County
Placerville
El Dorado County Fairgrounds
on Placerville Drive
916-622-5629

Humboldt County
Arcata
On the Square
707-722-4203

Eureka
Old Town
707-722-4203

Eureka Mall, Harris St.
707-722-4203

Marin County
Novato
Old Town, on Sherman
between Grant & Delong
415-456-3276

San Rafael
Marin County CFM
Marin Co. Civic Center Fairgrounds
415-456-3276

Downtown Farmers' Market
Festival, 4th St. between
Lootens & C St.
415-457-2266

Mendocino County
Boonville
Boonville Hotel parking lot
707-895-2461

Fort Bragg
Downtown
Laurel & Franklin
707-964-0536

Mendocino
Ukiah & Evergreen
next to Cafe Beaujolais
707-937-3322

Ukiah
Orchard Plaza Shopping Ctr.
Perkins & Orchard Ave.
707-468-1640

Willits
Commercial & Lenore Sts.
707-459-1871

Monterey County
Monterey
Monterey Peninsula College, off
Fremont Blvd.
408-663-3626

Salinas
Hartnell College
Central Ave. & Homestead
408-663-3626

Napa County
Napa
1st St. parking lot
707-963-7343

St. Helena
Napa Valley Railroad Depot
Railroad Ave. at Pine St.
707-963-7343

Nevada County
Grass Valley
County Fairgrounds, McCourtney Road
916-272-5257

Placer County
Auburn
Fulwiler at Hwy 49
916-663-0105

Loomis
Foothill Farmers Market
Taylor & Horseshoe Bar Rd.
916-663-0105

Tahoe City
Dollar Hill (Hwy 28) next
to Watermelon Patch
916-663-0105

Sacramento County
Carmichael
5701 Winding Way
916-929-9795

Sacramento
Central
Under Hwy 80, 8th & W Sts.,
State parking lot
916-363-3663

Country Club Centre
Rear parking garage
916-363-3663

Florin Mall
65th St., Parking lot behind Sears
916-363-3663

Plaza Park
10th & J Sts. across from City Hall
916-363-3663

Sunrise Mall
Sears parking lot
916-363-3663

San Francisco County
San Francisco
Alemany
100 Alemany Blvd.
415-647-9423

Heart of the City
U.N. Plaza, between
Leavenworth & Hyde
415-558-9455

San Joaquin County
Lodi
School St. between Pine &
Oak Sts.
209-943-1830

Stockton
Downtown, El Dorado & San
Joaquin, under Crosstown Hwy.
209-943-1830

The Mall
Corner of March Ln. & Pacific Avenue
209-943-1830

San Mateo County
Daly City
Serramonte-Hwy 280 & Serramonte Blvd.
in Macy's parking lot
415-798-7061

San Mateo
Fashion Island Shopping Center
415-798-7061

Redwood City
Redwood City Kiwanis
Farmers' Market
Parking lot, Winslow, south of Broadway
415-792-4103

Santa Clara County
Gilroy
Downtown
5th St between
Monterey & Eigleberry Sts.
408-842-6964

Los Altos
Loyola Corners Farmers Market
Parking plaza at Miramonte &
B St.
415-948-3366

Morgan Hill
Downtown
First & Monterey
408-779-5130

Palo Alto
Gilman St. behind downtown post office
415-325-2088

San Jose
Japan Town
8th & Jackson St.
408-298-4303

Prusch Park
Hwy 280 & King
408-926-5555

Town & Country Village
Winchester & Stevens
Creek Blvds.
415-798-7061

Santa Cruz County
Aptos
Cabrillo College on Soquel Drive
408-663-3626

Felton
Next to Post Office off Highway 9
408-335-9364

Santa Cruz
Corner of Pacific & Cathcart
Ford's parking lot
408-429-8433

Watsonville
Peck & Main Street
408-726-2521

Shasta County
Redding
Mt. Shasta Mall next to Dana Dr.
916-347-4627

Siskiyou County
Greenview
Scott Valley Feed Store
on Hwy 3
916-467-5726

Solano County
Fairfield
Texas St. between Taylor
& Jackson
707-425-3276

Vallejo
Downtown
Georgia & Sacramento
(Hwy 29 off Hwy 780)
415-456-3276

Sonoma County
Cloverdale
Veterans Memorial Bldg.
1st & Commercial Sts.
1 block west of Hwy 101
707-894-4623

Healdsburg
North & Vine, West plaza parking lot
707-433-6063

Petaluma
Downtown 4th & B
707-762-0344

Santa Rosa
Veterans Memorial Bldg.
707-523-0962

Downtown, 4th & B
707-538-7023

Downtown, City Hall
parking lot, Sonoma &
D Sts.
707-538-7023

Montgomery Village
Sonoma St. & Farmer's Ln.
707-538-7023

Sebastopol
McKinley St. at Petaluma
Ave., downtown
707-823-0823

Sonoma
Arnold Field parking lot,
(North of Depot Museum)
707-538-7023

Sutter County
Yuba City
Center St. between Plumas
& Shasta Sts., downtown
916-671-3346

Tehama County
Red Bluff
K-Mart parking lot, S. Main St.
916-527-7504

Trinity County
Hayford
Hayfork Park on Main St.
916-628-4242

Weaverville
Hwy 299 next to
Highland Art Center
916-623-6821

Yolo County
Davis
4th & C, Central Park
916-756-1695

Second St., Downtown
between E & C Sts.
916-756-1695

Winters
City parking lot, Railroad
St., between Abbey &
Main
916-795-2283

Woodland
2nd & Main St., Heritage Plaza
916-666-5269

SOUTHERN

Fresno County
Clovis
Pollasky between 4th & 5th
Sts., Old Town Clovis
209-298-5774

Fresno
Vineyard, 500 West
Shaw Ave. at Blackstone
209-222-0182

Reedley
G St. between 11th & 12th
209-638-5484

Imperial County

El Centro
Main St. between 5th & 6th
619-353-6771

Kern County

Bakersfield
College Center
Columbus & Haley
805-589-6589

Downtown, 30th & F Sts.
next to Pepper Tree Market
805-589-6589

Rosewood
1301 New Stine
805-589-6589

Shafter
Corner of James & Central
805-746-3982

Kings County

Lemoore
D Street between Fox &
Follett
209-923-4132

Hanford
Downtown on Irwin St.
between 6th & 7th
209-923-4125

Los Angeles County

Alhambra
Corner of Chico &
Stoneman, north of
Main Street
818-570-3205

Bellflower
Laurel & Bellflower
1/2 mile north of
Highway 91
310-804-1424

Burbank
3rd St. & Palm Ave.
Public parking lot
818-896-6539

Compton
Hub City, east side of
Alameda at Compton
310-537-5415

El Monte
Valley Blvd & Grenada
714-535-5694

Gardena
Hollypark Methodist Church
13000 South Van Ness
310-978-9693

Hermosa Beach
13th & Hermosa Ave.
310-379-1488

Highland Park
Sycamore Grove Park
4600 block of North
Figueroa
818-449-0179

Hollywood
Ivar Ave. between Selma
Ave. & Hollywood Blvd.
213-749-9551

Long Beach
The Promenade, between
Third & Broadway
310-433-3881

Dooley's parking lot,
Del Amo west of Long
Beach Blvd.
310-433-3881

Los Angeles
Adams & Vermont
St. Agnes Catholic Church
213-732-3610

Monrovia
Library Park at
Myrtle & Lime
818-449-0179

Norwalk
Alondra Blvd., west of
Pioneer across from
Excelsior High School
310-863-7365

Pasadena
City Hall
100 North Garfield
818-449-0179

Victory, Pasadena
High School, Paloma &
Sierra Madre
818-449-0179

Villa Parke neighborhood
center, 363 East Villa St.
818-449-0179

Pomona
On Pearl at North Garey
714-623-1031

Redondo Beach
End of Torrance Blvd.
at Redondo Beach Pier
310-735-2586

San Fernando Valley
14941 Devonshire between
Woodman & Sepulveda
818-361-3902

San Pedro
3rd Street between
Mesa & Centre
310-433-3881

Santa Monica
Arizona Ave. & 2nd St.
714-879-6669

South Gate
South Gate Park at
Tweedy & Walnut
213-774-0159

Torrance
Charles H. Wilson Park,
2200 block Crenshaw at
Jefferson
310-379-1488

Venice
Corner of Venice Blvd.
and Pacific Ave.
310-399-6690

West Hollywood
Plummer Park
7377 Santa Monica Blvd
213-854-7471

Whittier
12000 block of Bailey St.
between Greenleaf &
Comstock (uptown)
714-526-5814

Merced County
Gustine
5th St. between
3rd & 5th Avenues
209-854-3146

Merced
Farmers' Market Festival
Downtown on Main St.
between K and N
209-722-8820

Original Farmers' Market
N St. between 18th & 19th
209-722-3109

Original Farmers' Market
Sears parking lot, Olive &
R Streets
209-722-3109

Orange County
Costa Mesa
County Fairgrounds
88 Fair Drive
714-646-8342

Fullerton
Woodcrest Park
450 W. Orangethorpe at Richman
714-535-5694

Santa Ana
Fiesta Market Place
Bush & Third Sts.
714-535-5694

Riverside County
Palm Springs
Palm Canyon Dr. between
Tahquitz Cyn & Baristo Rd.
619-323-8265

Rialto
Downtown (Call for
more info)
714-421-7215

Riverside
Downtown on 5th St.
between Market & Orange
714-685-5940

Sears parking lot
Arlington at Streeter
714-685-5940

San Bernardino County
Colton
Fleming Park
La Cadena & 7th
714-685-5940

Redlands
State Street between
Orange & 7th
714-798-7548

Upland
2nd Avenue Market
between 9th & A Sts.
714-685-5940

San Diego County
Del Mar
City Hall parking lot
10th & Camino del Mar
619-749-3222

Escondido
North County CFM, Via
Rancho Parkway &
Sunset Drive
619-727-1471

Grand Ave. between
Broadway & Maple
619-726-8183

Mission Valley
Corner of Friars & Frazee
Rds.
619-741-3763

Pacific Beach
Promenade Shopping Mall
on Mission, 2 blocks
south of Grand
619-741-3763

San Marcos
San Marcos CFM
1020 San Marcos Blvd.,
west side of Old Calif.
restaurant row
619-743-0985

Temecula
Old Town
619-728-7343

Vista
Escondido & Eucalyptus
behind City Hall
619-726-8545

Main Street Festival
East Vista Way
619-726-8545

San Luis Obispo County
Arroyo Grande
Branch & Mason
City Hall parking lot
805-489-0889

Oak Park Plaza
Hwy 101 & Oak Plaza
805-489-0889

Atascadero
Entrada between El Camino
Real & Palma
805-927-4305

Baywood Park
Santa Maria & Second St.
805-238-2644

Cambria
Pinedorado parking lot in
West Village
805-927-4715

Morro Bay
Young's Giant Food
parking lot on
North Main St.
805-772-4250

625 Harbor Blvd.
805-772-4250

Paso Robles
14th & Spring Street
805-238-7056

San Luis Obispo
Downtown
Higuera St. at Chorro
805-544-9570

Central Coast Plaza
Gottschalk's parking lot
805-489-0889

Templeton
Templeton Park, on 6th
between Crocker & Country
805-238-6916

Santa Barbara County
Carpenteria
400 block of Linden Ave.
805-566-7004

Lompoc
Ocean & I Sts. public
parking lot
805-929-4192

Santa Barbara
Cota & Santa Barbara
805-563-0393

Old Town, 500 block
of State Street
805-563-0393

Santa Maria
Target parking lot, Miller
St. and Betteravia Rd.
805-929-4192

Stanislaus County
Ceres
4th & North (First Baptist
Church parking lot)
209-632-9322

Modesto
Next to the library on 16th St.
between H & I
209-632-9322

Turlock
West Main St. between
Market & Thor
209-632-9322

Tulare County
Tulare
Corner of K & San Joaquin
209-747-0095

Visalia
Sears parking lot
Mooney & Caldwell
209-747-0095

Downtown
Main St at Encina
209-747-0095

Tuolumne County
Sonora
Theall St. between
Stewart & Shepherd
209-532-2777

Ventura County
Camarillo
Old Downtown Camarillo
2220 Ventura Blvd.
805-484-9340

Ojai
On Matilija at signal
805-649-3078

Oxnard
Downtown Oxnard CFM
7th & B Sts.
805-984-4624

Thousand Oaks
Janss Mall at Wilbur Rd.
805-529-6266

Ventura
Downtown
Santa Clara & Figueroa
805-529-6266

Midtown at Main &
Mills, Montgomery Ward
parking lot
805-529-6266

California's Certified Farmers' Markets are places where farmers sell their crops, usually once a week, directly to the public. The certified Producer certificate posted at each seller's space is the customer's guarantee of buying directly from the grower, his family or employee.

For additional information and publications, call **916-654-0824,** or write: Direct Marketing Program, 1220 N Street, Room 225, Sacramento, CA 95814.

FARM TRAILS

Farm Trail organizations are composed of farmers in a specific area who sponsor the publication of a map indicating local farms that sell direct to consumers. When you write for a free copy of their map, be sure to enclose a self-addressed stamped envelope.

Alameda County Farm Trails
638 Enos Way, Livermore 94550
510-670-5200

224 West Winton Ave., Hayward 94544
510-449-1677

Apple Hill Growers
P.O. Box 494, Camino 95709
916-622-9595

Calaveras Farm Trails
P.O. Box 837, San Andreas 95249
209-754-4160

Central Valley Harvest Trails
P.O. Box 3070, Modesto 95353
209-522-7278

Coastside Harvest Trails
765 Main St., Half Moon Bay 94019
415-726-4485

Country Crossroads
1368 N. 4th St., San Jose 95112
408-453-0100

141 Monte Vista Ave., Watsonville 95076
408-724-1356

El Dorado Ranch Marketing & Rural Recreation Guide
542 Main St., Placerville 95667
916-621-5885

49er Fruit Trail
P.O. Box 317, Newcastle 95658
916-885-3005

Harvest Time in Brentwood
P.O. Box 773, Brentwood 94513
510-634-3344

Mendocino Farm Paths
303-C Talmage Rd., Ukiah 95482
707-462-6664

Napa County Farming Trails
4075 Solano Ave., Napa 94558
707-224-5403

Oak Glen Apple Growers
Box 1123, Yucaipa 92399
714-797-6833

Sacramento Farm Trails
4145 Branch Center Rd., Sacramento 95827
916-366-2013

S.L.O. County Farm Trails
1039 Chorro St., San Luis Obispo 93401
805-543-1323

Sierra Shepherds Sheep Trail
9043 Sky View Lane, Granite Bay 95661
916-791-2436

Sonoma County Farm Trails
P.O. Box 6032, Santa Rosa 95406
707-544-4728

Suisun Valley Farm Trails
2000 West Texas St., Fairfield 94533
707-429-6381

Tehachapi Apple Growers
P.O. Box 401, Tehachapi 93581
805-822-4180

Tulare Co. Harvest Trail
15908 Ave. 264, Visalia 93277
209-747-0095

Yosemite Apple Trails
P.O. Box 369, Oakhurst 93644
209-683-7766

Yuba-Sutter Ag Trails
P.O. Box 1429, Marysville 95901
916-743-6501

CALIFORNIA STATE RESOURCES AGENCY

1416 9th St., Sacramento 95814
Gordon Van Vleck, Secretary
916-445-5656   FAX 916-323-1972

California Energy Commission
1516 9th St., Sacramento 95814
Charles R. Imbrecht, Chairman
916-654-4996

Coastal Commission
45 Fremont St., San Francisco 94105
Peter Douglas, Executive Director
510-904-5200

Coastal Conservancy
1330 Broadway, Ste. 1100, Oakland 94612-2530
Peter Grenell, Executive Officer
510-464-1015

Colorado River Board
777 Fairmont Ave., Ste. 100
Glendale 97203-1035
Gerald R. Zimmerman, Executive Director
818-543-4676

Department of Conservation
1416-9th St., Room 1320
Edward Heidig, Director
916-322-1080

Department of Fish & Game
1416-9th St., 12th Floor
Peter F. Bontadelli, Director
916-653-7667

Department of Forestry & Fire Protection
1416-9th St., 15th Floor
Richard Wilson, Director
916-445-3976

Department of Parks & Recreation
1416-9th St., 14th Floor
Henry R. Agonia, Director
916-653-8380

Department of Water Resources
1416-9th St., Room 115-1
David Kennedy, Director
916-653-7007

Reclamation Board
1416 9th St., Room 455-6, Sacramento 95814
Ray Barsch, General Manager
916-653-5434

State Lands Commission
1807 13th St., Sacramento 95814
Charles Warren, Executive Officer
916-322-4105

California Environmental Protection Agency
Cal-EPA

555 Capitol Mall, Ste. 235, Sacramento, CA 95814
FAX 916-445-6401

EXECUTIVE OFFICE:

James M. Strock, Secretary
916-445-3846

Brian A. Runkel, Chief of Staff
916-445-3846

Michael Kahoe, Assistant Secretary
916-322-5844

Charles M. Shulock, Assistant Secretary
916-324-8124

Vacant, Communications Director
916-324-9671

DEPARTMENT OF PESTICIDE REGULATIONS

Jim Wells, Interim Director
916-654-0551

Environmental Monitoring/Pest Management
Ronald Oshima, Chief
916-654-1144

Information Services
Richard Knoll, Chief
916-654-1353

Medical Toxicology
Larry Nelson, Chief
916-654-1285

Pesticide Enforcement
Doug Okumura, Chief
916-654-0831

Pesticide Registration
Tobi Jones, Chief
916-654-0567

Worker Health & Safety
Robert Krieger, Senior Toxicologist
916-654-0455

DEPARTMENT OF TOXIC SUBSTANCES CONTROL

William F. Soo Hoo, Interim Director
916-323-9723

INTEGRATED WASTE MANAGEMENT BOARD

Ralph Chandler, Executive Director
916-322-3330
Michael Frost, Chairman
916-322-3330

AIR RESOURCES BOARD

James D. Boyd, Executive Officer
916-445-4383
Jananne Sharpless, Chairperson
916-322-5840

STATE WATER RESOURCES CONTROL BOARD

Walter G. Pettit, Executive Officer
916-657-0941
W. Don Maughan, Chairman
916-445-3993

OFFICE OF ENVIRONMENTAL HEALTH HAZARD ASSESSMENT

Steven A. Book, Interim Director
916-445-6900

HAZARDOUS MATERIALS

Steve Hanna, Chief
916-324-9924

OFFSHORE DEVELOPMENT

Vacant, Grant Manager
916-324-7584
Jo Gilpin, Executive Secretary
916-324-3706

United State Department of Agriculture

AGRICULTURAL RESEARCH SERVICE—MAJOR LABORATORIES, FIELD STATIONS AND LOCATIONS IN CALIFORNIA

Pacific West Area Office
800 Buchanan Street, Albany 94710
FAX 510-559-5779
Dr. Robert J. Reginato, Director
510-559-6060

Vacant,
Associate Director
510-559-6071

Mr. W. Ralph Nave
Assistant Director
510-559-6063

Mr. Chester A. Reder
Area Administrative Officer
510-559-6000

Western Regional Research Center
800 Buchanan Street, Albany 94710
FAX 510-559-5779

Western Regional Research Center
Dr. Antoinette Betschart, Center Director
510-559-5600

Food Quality Research
Dr. Robert Sayre, Research Leader
510-559-5650

Food Safety Research
Dr. Kenneth Stevens, Research Leader
510-559-5610

Plant Development-Quality Research
Glenn Fuller, Research Leader
510-559-5750

Plant Development-Productivity Research
Dr. William Hurkman, Acting Research Leader
510-559-5700

Plant Protection Research Unit
Dr. L. Jurd, Research Leader
510-559-5800

Processing Biotechnology Research Unit
Dr. N. Goodman, Research Leader
510-559-5850

Process Chemistry & Engineering Research Unit
Dr. Attila Pavlath, Research Leader
510-559-5620

Plant Gene Expression Center
800 Buchanan Street, Albany 94710
FAX 510-559-5678

Dr. Gerald G. Still, Director
510-559-5900

USDA LABS AT UNIVERSITY OF CALIFORNIA, DAVIS:
3116 Wickson Hall, Davis 95616

Aquatic Weed Control Research
Dr. Lars W.J. Anderson, Research Leader
916-752-6260

Plant Pathology
Dr. S.M. Mircetich, Research Leader
916-752-1919

National Clonal Germplasm Repository
Dr. Katie Rigert, Curator
916-752-6504

USDA LABS AT FRESNO:
2021 S. Peach Ave., Fresno 93747

Horticultural Crops Research Laboratory
Dr. P.V. Vail, Director
209-443-3020

Postharvest Quality and Genetics Research Unit
Dr. Louis Aung, Research Leader
209-453-3160

Water Management Research Laboratory
Dr. Claude Phene, Director/Research Leader
209-453-3101

USDA LABS AT RIVERSIDE:
4500 Glenwood Drive, Riverside 92501
FAX 714-781-7060

U.S. Salinity Laboratory
Dr. J.D. Rhoades, Director
714-369-4816

Soil Physics Research
Martinus T. Van Genuchten, Research Leader
714-369-4847

Plant Science Research
Dr. Michael D. Shannon, Research Leader
714-369-4831

Soil and Water Chemistry Research
Dr. J.D. Rhoades, Research Leader
714-369-4816

Pesticide Management Research Unit
Dr. William Spencer, Research Leader
714-369-4846

OTHER USDA RESEARCH LOCATIONS:

Western Human Nutrition Research Center
P.O. Box 29997
Presidio of San Francisco 94129
Dr. J.M. Iacono, Center Director
415-556-9697   FAX 415-546-1432

Bioenergetics Research
Dr. Darshan Kelly, Research Leader
415-556-5800

Micronutrients Research
Dr. Robert Jacob, Research Leader
415-556-5655

Biochemistry Research
Dr. J.M. Iancono, Research Leader
415-556-3531

Cotton and Other Agronomic Crops Production
17053 Shafter Ave., Shafter 93263
Dr. Claude Phene, Research Leader &
Acting Location Coordinator
805-746-6361

Sugarbeet Production Research
1636 E. Alisal St., Salinas 93905
Dr. J.E. Duffus, Research Leader &
Location Coordinator
408-433-2253

Vegetable Production Research
1636 E. Alisal St., Salinas 93905
Dr. E.J. Ryder, Research Leader
408-443-2253

Irrigated Desert Research Station
4151 Highway 86, Brawley 92227
Clifford Brown, Superintendent
619-344-4184

Fruit and Vegetable Chemistry Research
262 S. Chester Ave., Pasadena 91106
Dr. Robert Horowitz, Research Leader &
Location Coordinator
818-796-0239

United States Department of Agriculture Major Program Offices

California State Agriculture Stabilization & Conservation Service (Farm Loans & Commodity Programs)
1303 J St., Ste. 300, Sacramento 95814
John G. Smythe, State Executive Director
916-551-1801   FAX 916-442-2097

County ASCS Offices

Alpine-Inyo-Mono
1694 County Rd., P.O. Box 1329
Minden, Nevada 89423
Harvey Neill, County Executive Director
702-782-3661

Butte
463-B Oro Dam Boulevard, Oroville 95965
Vacant, County Executive Director
916-534-0112

Colusa
100 Sunrise Blvd., Suite D
Colusa 95932
Gary Souza, County Executive Director
916-458-5131

Contra Costa-Alameda
5554 Clayton Road, Room 4, Concord 94521
Richard Neves, County Executive Director
510-672-4949

Fresno
4625 W. Jennifer, Suite 109
Fresno 93722
Robert L. Briney, County Executive Director
209-487-5225

Glenn
132-A North Enright, Willows 95988
Don Perez, County Executive Director
916-934-4669

Humboldt-Del Norte
5630 S. Broadway, P.O. Box 4908
Eureka 95501
Donald G. Buchanan, County Executive Director
707-442-6058

Imperial
380 N. 8th St., Suite 15, El Centro 92243
Marilyn J. McAbee, County Executive Director
714-352-3531

Kern
5500 Ming Ave., Ste. 170, Bakersfield 93309
Gregg Hindman, County Executive Director
805-861-4125

Kings
Kings County Government Center
680 Campus Drive, Hanford 93230
Dave Unruh, County Executive Director
209-582-1071

Lassen-Plumas-Sierra
50-A Hall Street, Susanville 96130
George A. Moran, County Executive Director
916-257-4127

Los Angeles-Orange-San Bernardino
45116 N. 13th Street West, Lancaster 93534
James Tegeler, County Executive Director
805-942-9549

Madera
425 No. Gateway Drive, Suite E
Madera 93637
Lorraine Valenzuela, County Executive Director
209-674-4628

Mendocino-Lake
405 Orchard Avenue, Ukiah 95482
Vacant, County Executive Director
707-468-9225

Merced-Mariposa
2135 W. Wardrobe Ave., Ste. B
Merced 95340
Chris Keeler, County Executive Director
209-722-4119

Modoc
1030 N. Main, Ste. 103, Alturas 96101
Chris Lauppe, County Executive Director
916-233-4391

Monterey-San Mateo-Santa Cruz
635 So. Sanborn Road, Suite 6
Salinas 93901
Vivian Soffa, County Executive Director
408-424-7377

Placer-Nevada-El Dorado
251 Auburn Ravine Road, Suite 203
Auburn 95603
Wilma C. Powers, County Executive Director
916-885-6505

Riverside-San Diego
45691 Monroe Street, Suite 4, Indio 92201
Greg Tonkinson, County Executive Director
619-347-3675

Sacramento-Amador
65 Quinta Court, Suite A, Sacramento 95823
Connie Skinner, County Executive Director
916-682-7821

San Benito-Santa Clara
253 6th Street, Hollister 95023
Vacant, County Executive Director
408-637-4360

San Joaquin-Calaveras
1222 Monaco Court, Suite 27
Stockton 95207
Jeff Yasui, County Executive Director
209-946-6241

San Luis Obispo
4401 El Camino Real, Suite A
Atascadero 93422
Pat Kittle, County Executive Director
805-466-1551

Santa Barbara-Ventura
254 E.. Hwy 246, Suite D
Buellton 93427
Vacant, County Executive Director
805-688-2727

Shasta-Trinity
3179 Bechelli Lane, Room 106
Redding 96001
Joe Gassaway, County Executive Director
916-246-5253

Siskiyou
215 Executive Court, Suite B, Yreka 96097
Vacant, County Executive Director
916-842-6123

Solano-Napa
1170 N. Lincoln St., Suite 109
Dixon, 95620
Heidi C. Pfaendler, County Executive Director
916-678-1931

Sonoma-Marin
777 Sonoma Avenue, Fed. Bldg., Room 212
Santa Rosa 95404
Beverly Eddinger, County Executive Director
707-525-9058

Stanislaus-Tuolumne
1701 Coffee Road, Ste. 2, Modesto 95355
Victor Lloyd Myers, County Executive Director
209-523-4576

Sutter-Yuba
1531 Ste. A Butte House Road, Yuba City 95991
Mark Renfree, County Executive Director
916-671-0850

Tehama
2 Sutter Street, Suite C, Red Bluff 96080
Vacant, County Executive Director
916-527-3013

Tulare
3135 So. Mooney Blvd., Suite B
Visalia 93277
Gene L. Bennett, County Executive Director
209-734-5814

Yolo

221 W. Court, Suite 3 B
Woodland 95695
Neil H. Busch, County Executive Director
916-662-3986

FARMERS HOME ADMINISTRATION

194 W. Main Street, Suite F
Woodland 95695-2915
Richard E. Mallory, Director
916-666-3382   FAX 916-666-1470

District Offices

1900 Churn Creek Road, Suite 119
Redding 96002-0245
Roger Trindade, Director
916-246-5393   FAX 916-246-5409

1222 Monaco Court, Suite 19
Stockton 95207-6793
Robert P. Anderson, Director
209-946-6455   FAX 209-476-8756

777 Sonoma Avenue
Room 213, Santa Rosa 95404-4731
Paul B. Rice, Director
707-526-6797   FAX 707-526-8942

3137 S. Mooney Blvd.
Visalia 93277-7398
Richard Brassfield, Director
209-732-4123   FAX 209-732-3481

21160 Box Springs Road, Suite 105
Moreno Valley 92557
Raymond H. Gardner, Director
714-276-6766   FAX 714-369-6289

County Offices

204 W. 12th Street, Suite E
Alturas, 96101-3211
James Colbert, Supervisor
916-233-4615

582 Camino Mercado
Arroyo Grande 93420-1816
Vacant, Supervisor
805-489-6151

251 Auburn Ravine Rd., Suite 103
Auburn 95603-4294
Ms. Donna J. Gordy, Supervisor
916-885-7081

5500 Ming Ave., Suite 155
Bakersfield 93309-8490
Nathan E. Maragoni, Supervisor
805-861-4221

1681 Main St., Room 412
El Centro 92243-2285
James A. Jutson, Supervisor
619-352-3314

5630 S. Broadway
P.O. Box 4901
Eureka 95502-4907
Robert A. Noble, Supervisor
707-443-6714

4625 W. Jennifer St., Suite 126
Fresno 93722
Tom D. Roberts, Supervisor
209-487-5010

680 Campus Dr., Suite D
Hanford 93230-9505
James San Bourin, Supervisor
209-584-9227

45-691 Monroe St., Suite 1
Indio 92201
Christopher D. Ketner, Supervisor
619-342-4624

2135 W. Wardrobe Ave., Suite A
Merced 95340-6490
Kenneth R. Sevick
209-723-0475

1620 N. Carpenter Rd., Suite 47
Modesto 95351-1153
Roy V. Burnett
209-526-8136

463-L Oro Dam Blvd., Ste. B
Oroville 95965-5791
Ms. Michele D. Larrick
916-533-4401

2 Sutter St., Suite B
Red Bluff 96080-4388
Edwin A. Amen
916-527-1013

3179 Bechelli Lane, Ste. 109
Redding 96002-2098
Leonard Thompson
916-246-5244

65 Quinta Court, Suite D
Sacramento 95823-4386
David E. Sander
916-551-1678

635 S. Sanborn Rd., Suite 18
Salinas 93901-4533
Gustavo Cairo, Jr.
408-757-5294

777 Sonoma Ave., Room 212
Santa Rosa 95404-4799
Ms. Terry L. Mahoney
707-526-6883

1222 Monaco Court, Ste. 28
Stockton 95207-6790
Frank J. Risso, Jr.
209-946-6244

1963 E. Tulare Ave.
Tulare 93274-3297
Simon (Fred) Smith
209-686-8681

405 Orchard Ave.
Ukiah 95482-5090
Gilbert L. Naong
707-462-2916

15028 - 7th St., Suite 2
Victorville 92392-3859
Brooks Whitlock
619-245-8658

3135 S. Mooney Blvd., Ste. A
Visalia 93277-7360
Ms. Gayle A. Hoskinson
209-734-1309

132 N. Enright, Ste. C
Willows 95988-2697
Ms. Elizabeth Roberson
916-934-4614

215 Executive Court, Ste. C,
Yreka 96097-2692
Robert G. Reed, II
916-842-5774

1531-B Butte House Road
Yuba City 95991-2293
Ms. Mary McLean
916-673-4347

Food and Nutrition Service
550 Kearny Street, Room 400
San Francisco 94108-2518
Ms. Sharon Levinson, Regional Administrator
415-705-1310   FAX 415-705-1364

Forest Service
Pacific Southwest Region (Region 5)
630 Sansome Street, Room 559
San Francisco 94111
Ronald E. Stewart, Regional Forester
415-705-2874   FAX 415-705-2836

Fruit & Vegetable Division:

Market News Branch (Market Reports)
630 Sansome Street, Room 727
San Francisco 94111
Frederick Teensma, Officer in Charge
415-705-1300   FAX 415-705-1301

Marketing Field Office (Marketing Orders)
2202 Monterey St., Ste. 102B, Fresno 93721
Gary Olson, Officer in Charge
209-487-5901

Soil Conservation Service
2121-C 2nd St., Davis 95616
Pearlie S. Reed, State Conservationist
916-449-2848   FAX 916-758-8181

The Soil and Water Conservation Society, California Chapter
2121-C 2nd Street, Davis 95616
Phil Hogan, President
916-449-2843

Yolo Watch
2121-C 2nd Street, Davis 95616
Phil Hogan, President
916-449-2841

UNITED STATES DEPARTMENT OF THE INTERIOR

Bureau of Land Management—California State Office
Federal Building
2800 Cottage Way, Sacramento 95825
Ed Hastey, State Director
916-978-4743   FAX 916-978-4715

Bureau of Reclamation—California State Office
Federal Building, Room W-1105
2800 Cottage Way, Sacramento 95825
Roger K. Patterson, Regional Director
916-978-5135   FAX 916-978-5284

FEDERAL INFORMATION (For Information Regarding Other U.S.A. offices)

FOR WRITTEN INQUIRIES:
Federal Information Center
P.O. Box 600
Cumberland, MD 21501-0600
1-800-726-4995

PART IV

Fair Associations

Alameda County Fair
4501 Pleasanton Ave., Pleasanton 94566
Peter Bailey, Manager
510-846-2881

Amador County Fair
P.O. Box 9, Plymouth 95669
Ralph L. Clark, Manager
209-245-6921

Antelope Valley Fair & Alfalfa Festival
155 East Avenue "I", Lancaster 93534
James A. Pacini, Manager
805-948-6060

Big Fresno Fair
1121 Chance Ave., Fresno 93702
Ron Miller, Manager
209-453-3247

Butte County Fair
P.O. Box 308, Gridley 95948
Lowell Walgenbach, Manager
916-846-3626

Calaveras County Fair & Jumping Frog Jubilee
P.O. Box 96, Angels Camp 95222
Tawni Tesconi, Manager
209-736-2561

California Exposition & State Fair
P.O. Box 15649, Sacramento 95852
Joe Barkett, Manager
916-924-2061

California Mid-State Fair
P.O. Box 8, Paso Robles 93447
Maynard Potter, Manager
805-239-0655

California Mid-Winter Fair
200 E. Second St., Imperial 92251
Maxine Killiam, Manager
619-355-1181

Chico Christmas Fair
P.O. Box 1158, Chico 95927
Thomas DiGrazia, Manager
916-895-4666

Chowchilla-Madera County Fair
P.O. Box 597, Chowchilla 93610
Jim Johnson, Manager
209-665-3728

Cloverdale Citrus Fair
#1 Citrus Drive
Cloverdale 95425
Gary McDonald, Manager
707-894-3992

Colorado River County Fair
11995 Olive Lake Blvd., Blythe 92225-9454
Jay L. Abbs, Manager
619-922-9183

Colusa County Fair
P.O. Box 240, Colusa 95932
Roger Gibbs, Manager
916-458-2641

Colusa Holiday Fair and Craft Show
P.O. Box 240, Colusa 95932
Roger Gibbs, Manager
916-458-2641

Contra Costa County Fair
P.O. Box 1378, 1201 W. 10th St., Antioch 94509
Chris Baldwin, Manager
510-757-4400

Del Norte County Fair
P.O. Box 1063, Crescent City 95531
Randy Hatfield, Manager
707-464-9556

Desert Empire Fair
520 S. Richmond Rd., Ridgecrest 93555
Earl Powers, Manager
619-375-8000

Dixon May and Christmas Faire
P.O. Box 459, Dixon 95620
John Campbell, Manager
916-678-5529

Eastern Sierra Tri-County Fair
P.O. Box 608, Bishop 93514
Ned Londo, Manager
619-873-3588

El Dorado County Fair
P.O. Box 1537, Placerville 95667
Susan Clark, Manager
916-621-5860

Farmers Fair of Riverside County
18700 Perris Lake Rd., Perris 92370
Lindal Graff, Manager
714-657-4221

Festival at the Lake
1630 Webster Street, Oakland 94612
Sharon Jensen, Manager
510-464-1061

Glenn County Fair
P.O. Box 667, Orland 95963
Paul Briggs, Manager
916-865-4418

Gold Country Fair
P.O. Box 5527, Auburn 95604-5527
Hank Maule, Manager
916-885-6281

Grand National Livestock Exposition, Horse Show and Rodeo
P.O. Box 34206, San Francisco 94134
Mike Wegher, Manager
415-469-6000

Great Snail Festival
16040 Amar Rd., City of Industry 91744
Carol Spoelstra, Manager
818-330-9496

Great Western Livestock & Expo
215 E. Slpine Ave., Tulare 93274
John Alkire, Manager
209-686-4707

Humboldt County Fair
P.O. Box 637, Ferndale 95536
Stuart Titus, Manager
707-786-9511

Inter-Mountain Fair of Shasta County
P.O. Box 10, McArthur 96056
Dennis Hoffman, Manager
916-336-5695

Josh's Jamboree
520 South Richmond Road, Ridgecrest 93555
Carl Powers, Manager
619-375-8000

Junior Grand National Livestock Exposition, Horse Show and Rodeo
P.O. Box 34206, San Francisco 94134
Mike Wegher, Manager
415-469-6000

Kern County Fair
Kern County Country Horse Fair
1142 South "P" St., Bakersfield 93307
Mike Treacy, Manager
805-833-4900

Kings District Fair
P.O. Box 14, Hanford 93230
Darell Breedlove, Manager
209-584-3318

Lake County Fair
P.O. Box 70, Lakeport 95453
Jack Mather, Manager
707-263-6181

Lassen County Fair
195 Russell Ave., Susanville 96130
Tom Henderson, Manager
916-257-4104

Lodi Grape Festival & National Wine Show
P.O. Box 848, Lodi 95241
Graeme Stewart, Manager
209-369-2771

Los Angeles County Fair
P.O. Box 2250, Pomona 91769
Ralph Hinds, Manager
714-623-3111

Madera District Fair
P.O. Box 837, Madera 93639
1850 W. Cleveland Ave.
Tom Musser, Manager
209-674-8511

Marin County Fair
Fairgrounds, San Rafael 94903
Yolanda F. Sullivan, Manager
415-499-6400

Mariposa County Fair
5007 Fairgrounds Dr., Mariposa 95338
Vacant, Manager
209-966-2432 or 209-966-3686

Mendocino County Fair & Apple Show
P.O. Box 458, Boonville 95415
William F. "Jim" Clow, Manager
707-895-3011

Merced County Fair
P.O. Box 1352, Merced 95341
Anthony Leo, Manager
209-722-1506

Merced County Spring Fair—Los Banos
P.O. Box 71, Los Banos 93635
James Shasky, Manager
209-826-5166

Modoc District Fair
P.O. Box 26, Cedarville 96104
Paul Gillingham, Manager
916-279-2315

Monterey County Fair
2004 Fairground Rd., Monterey 93940
Perry Slocum, Manager
408-372-5863

Monterey National Horse Show
2004 Fairground Rd., Monterey 93940
Perry Slocum, Manager
408-372-5863

Mother Lode Fair
220 Southgate Dr., Sonora 95370
David Massa, Manager
209-532-7428

Napa County Fair
P.O. Box 344, Calistoga 94515
Mike Kenney, Manager
707-942-5111

Napa Town & Country Fair
& Spring Fair
575 Third St., Napa 94558
Dorothy Lind, Manager
707-253-4900

National Orange Show
689 S. "E" St., San Bernardino 92408
Ester Armstrong, Manager
714-383-5444

Nevada County Fair
P.O. Box 2687, Grass Valley 95945-2687
Edward Scofield, Manager
916-273-6217

Orange County Fair
88 Fair Dr., Costa Mesa 92626
Norbert Bartosik, Manager
714-751-3247

Placer County Fair
800 All American City Blvd., Roseville 95678
Vacant, Manager
916-786-2023

Plumas County Fair
P.O. Box 957, Quincy 95971
Beverly Wood, Manager
916-283-6272

Redwood Acres Fair
P.O. Box 6576, Eureka 95502-6576
3750 Harris Street, Eureka 95501
Robert Alkire, Manager
707-445-3037

Redwood Empire Fair/Spring Fair
P.O. Box 744, Ukiah 95482
William Pearce, Manager
707-462-3884

Riverside County's National Date Festival
46-350 Arabia St., Indio 92201
Craig Manning, Executive Director
619-342-8247

Sacramento County Fair—Cal Expo
P.O. Box 255252, Sacramento 95865
1600 Exposition Blvd., Sacramento 95815
Ann Steiger, Manager
916-924-2076

Salinas Valley Fair
625 Division St., King City 93930
Paul Slocum, Manager
408-385-3243

San Benito County Fair
P.O. Box 790, Hollister 95024
Kelley J. Ferreira, Manager
408-628-3421

San Benito County Saddle Horse Show
and Rodeo
P.O. Box 56, Hollister 95023
Jim McConnell, Manager
408-628-3545

San Bernardino County Fair
14800 Seventh St., Victorville 92392
Michael Sullivan, Interim Manager
619-951-2200

San Fernando Valley Fair
7247 Hayvenhurst Ave., Unit A-9
Van Nuys 91406
Dale Coons-Mintz, Manager
818-373-4500

San Francisco Fair & Exposition
455 Golden Gate Ave., Ste. 2095
San Francisco 94012
Skip Conrad, Manager
415-557-8758

San Joaquin County Fair
P.O. Box 6310, Stockton 95206
Forrest White, Manager
209-466-5041

San Mateo County Fair
P.O. Box 1027, San Mateo 94403
John Root, Manager
415-574-3247

Santa Barbara County Fair &
Horse Show
937 S. Thornburg St., Santa Maria 93454
John Burke, Manager
805-925-8824

Santa Barbara Exposition & Fair
& Flower Show
P.O. Box 3006, Santa Barbara 93130-3006
Selma Harris, Manager
805-687-0766

Santa Barbara National Amateur Horse Show
P.O. Box 3006, Santa Barbara 93130-3006
Selma Harris, Manager
805-687-0766

Santa Barbara National Horse Show
P.O. Box 3006, Santa Barbara 93130
Selma Harris, Manager
805-687-0766

Santa Clara County Fair
Santa Clara County Harvest Fair
Santa Clara County Holiday Fair
344 Tully Rd., San Jose 95111
Kim Petersen, Manager
408-295-3050

Santa Cruz County Fair
2601 E. Lake Ave., Watsonville 95076
John Kegebein, Manager
408-724-5671

Shasta District Fair
P.O. Box 605, Anderson 96007
Mark Campbell, Manager
916-365-2516

Silver Dollar Fair
P.O. Box 1158, Chico 95927
Thomas DiGrazia, Manager
916-895-4666

Siskiyou Golden Fair
1712 Fair Lane Rd., Yreka 96097
Ron Lillard, Manager
916-842-2767

Solano County Fair
900 Fairground Dr., Vallejo 94589
Bob Dunlap, Manager
707-644-4401

Sonoma County Fair
P.O. Box 1536, Santa Rosa 95403
Jim Moore, Manager
707-545-4200

Sonoma-Marin Fair
P.O. Box 182, Petaluma 94952
Beverly Wilson, Manager
707-763-0931

**Southern California Exposition/
Horse Show—Del Mar**
2260 Jimmy Durante, Del Mar 92014
Roger Vitaich, Manager
619-755-1161

Stanislaus County Fair
900 N. Broadway, Turlock 95380
Robert W. Walker, Manager
209-668-1333

Sun Country Fair
P.O. Box 70, Red Bluff 95080
Bert Owens, Manager
916-527-5920

Trinity County Fair
P.O. Box 880, Hayfork 96041
Jerry Fulton, Manager
916-628-5223

Tulare County Fair
215 E. Alpine, Tulare 93274
John Alkire, Manager
209-686-4707

Tulelake-Butte Valley Fair
P.O. Box 866, Tulelake 96134
Cindy Wright, Manager
916-667-2914

Ventura County Fair
Seaside Park, 10 W. Harbor Blvd.
Ventura 93001
Mike Paluszak, Manager
805-658-3376

Yolo County Fair
P.O. Box 826, Woodland 95695
Ron Maraviov, Manager
916-662-5393

Yuba-Sutter Fair
422 Franklin Ave., Yuba City 95991
Judy Habel, Manager
916-674-1280

PART V
California Agricultural Publications

Ag Alert
1601 Exposition Blvd., Sacramento 95815
916-924-4140   FAX 916-923-5318

Agribusiness Fieldman
4974 E. Clinton Way, Suite 123
Fresno 93727-1558
209-252-7000   FAX 209-252-7387

Agribusiness Fresh Fruit and Raisin News
612 N St., P.O. Box 669, Sanger 93657
209-875-4585

Agriculture and Natural Resources
University of California
6701 San Pablo Avenue
Oakland 94608-1239
510-642-2341   FAX 510-643-5470

Alameda County Farm Bureau News
638 Enos Way, Livermore 94550
510-449-1677

Almond Facts
P.O. Box 1768, Sacramento 95812
916-442-0771

Amador County Farm Bureau Newsletter
34-C Summit Street, Jackson 95642
209-223-0951

American Food & Ag Exporter Magazine
c/o A.G. Coallier Publishing Co., Inc.
1060 Fulton Mall, Suite 1202
Fresno 93721
209-237-1167   FAX 209-237-0489

Arabian Horse World
824 San Antonio Ave., Palo Alto 94303
415-856-0500

Aquatic Farming
P.O. Box 1004, Niland 92257
619-359-3474

B.L.M. Newsbeat
Federal Office Building
2800 Cottage Way, Room E-2841
Sacramento 95825
916-978-4746

Bottles and Bins
Charles Krug Winery
P.O. Box 191, St. Helena 94574
707-963-2761

Butte County Farm Bureau Bulletin
2580 Feather River Blvd., Oroville 95965
916-533-1473

Calaveras County Farm Bureau Newsletter
P.O. Box 490, Angels Camp 95222
209-736-4666

California Agribusiness Dairyman
612 N St., P.O. Box 669
Sanger 93657
209-875-4585

California Agriculture
University of California,
300 Lakeside Drive, 6th Floor
Oakland 94612-3560
510-987-0044   FAX 510-987-0672

California-Arizona Cotton
4974 E. Clinton Way, Ste. 123
Fresno 93727-1558
209-252-7000   FAX 209-252-7387

California-Arizona Farm Press
83 E. Shaw Ave., Ste. 250, Fresno 93710
209-221-8421

California Cattleman
1221 H Street, Sacramento 95814
916-444-0845

California Christmas Tree Growers Bulletin
1451 Danville Blvd., Suite 102
Alamo 94507
510-837-7463   FAX 510-837-9588

California Country
1601 Exposition Blvd., Sacramento 95815
916-924-4140   FAX 916-923-5318

California Farmer
2300 Clayton Road, Ste. 1360
Concord 94520
510-687-1662

California Freestone Peach Association Newsletter
P.O. Box 3004, Modesto 95353
209-538-2372

California Food
P.O. Box 4044, Los Angeles 90051
818-703-6177

California Fruit Grower
Blue Anchor Building, P.O. Box 15498
Sacramento 95851-9989
916-929-3050

California Grange News
2101 Stockton Blvd., Sacramento 95817
916-454-5805

California Grower
7360 Rifleman Road, Moorpark 93021
805-529-3495

California Pear Growers Newsletter
77 Cadillac Drive, Suite 100, Sacramento 95825
916-924-0530   FAX 916-924-0904

California Prune News
5990 Stoneridge Dr., Ste. 101
Pleasanton 94588
510-734-0150

California Tomato Growers Association
P.O. Box 7398, Stockton 95267-0398
209-478-1761

Citrograph
4974 E. Clinton Way, Suite 123, Fresno 93727-1558
209-252-7000   FAX 209-252-7387

Citrus & Vegetable
4974 E. Clinton Way, Suite 123, Fresno 93727-1558
209-252-7000   FAX 209-252-7387

Cling Peach Quarterly
P.O. Box 7001, Lafayette 94549-7010
510-284-9171

Colusa County Sodbuster
P.O. Box 459, Williams 95987
916-473-2505

Contra Costa County Farm Bureau Newsletter
5554 Clayton Road, Concord 94521
510-672-5115

Dairyman
P.O. Box 819, Corona 91718
714-735-2730   FAX 714-735-2460

El Dorado County Farm Bureau News
2460 Headington Rd., Placerville 95667
916-622-7773

Focus
Metropoliton Water District of Southern California
P.O. Box 54153, Los Angeles 90054-0153
213-250-6000

Forest Industries
600 Harrison St., San Francisco 94107
415-905-2200

Fresno County Agriculture Today
1274 West Hedges, Fresno 93728
209-237-0263

Glenn County Farm Bureau News
501 Walker St., Orland 95963
916-865-9636

Grape Growers
4974 E. Clinton Way, Suite 123
Fresno 93727-1558
209-252-7000   FAX 209-252-7387

HazNet
c/o Capital Reports
921-11th St., Ste. 701, Sacramento 95814
916-441-4427

Hot Irons (California Cattleman's Association)
1221 H Street, Sacramento 95814
916-444-0845

Imperial County Farm Bureau News
1000 Broadway, El Centro 92243
619-352-3831

Inside Waste
c/o Capitol Report
921-11th Street, Suite 701
Sacramento 95814
916-441-4427

Inyo-Mono County Farm Bureau Newsletter
P.O. Box 1803, Bishop 93514
619-933-2247

Kern County Farm News
P.O. Box 2425, Bakersfield 93303
805-323-7897

Kings County Farm Bureau News
870 Greenfield Ave., Hanford 93230
209-584-3557

Kiwifruit Growers of California Newsletter
7300 Lincolnshire Dr., Sacramento 95823
916-427-1544

Lake County Farm Bureau News
65 Soda Bay Rd., Lakeport 95453
707-263-0911

Landscape Magazine
4974 E. Clinton Way, Suite 123
Fresno 93727-1558
209-252-7000   FAX 209-252-7387

Lassen County Farm Bureau Newsletter
626 Main St., Susanville 96130
916-257-7242

Madera County Farm Bureau News
13314 Road 26, Madera 93637
209-674-8871

Mariposa County Farm Bureau News
P.O. Box 1297, Mariposa 95338
209-966-3848

Meat & Poultry Magazine
P.O. Box 1059, Mill Valley 94942
510-388-7575   FAX 510-388-4961

Mendocino County Farm Bureau News
303-C Talmage Road, Ukiah 95482
707-462-6664

Merced County Farm Bureau News
P.O. Box 1232, Merced 95341
209-723-3001

Modoc County Farm Bureau Newsletter
P.O. Box 1692, Alturas 96101
916-233-3276

Monterey County Farm Bureau Farm Focus
512 Pajaro St., Salinas 93901
408-422-9063

Napa County Farm Bureau Newsletter
4075 Solano Avenue, Napa 94558
707-224-5403   FAX 707-224-7836

Nevada County Farm Bureau Newsletter
P.O. Box 27, Grass Valley 95945
916-268-3214

Nut Grower
4974 E. Clinton Way, Suite 123
Fresno 93727-1558
209-252-7000   FAX 209-252-7387

On the Deck
California Agricultural Aircraft Assn.
2150 River Plaza Dr., Ste. 315
Sacramento 95833-3880
916-641-1171   FAX 916-924-1554

Orange County Farm Bureau News
2512 Chambers Rd., Ste. 203, Tustin 92680
714-573-0374

Pacific Fruit News
P.O. Box 460, 41 Copper Meadows Drive
Copperopolis 95228
209-785-3377

Pacific Coast Nurseryman
306 W. Foothill Blvd., P.O. Box 1477
Glendora 91740
818-914-3916

Peach Fuzz
P.O. Box 7001, Lafayette 94549
510-284-9171

Placer County Farm Bureau News
P.O. Box 317, Newcastle 95658
916-663-2929

Riverside County Agriculture
21160 Box Springs Road, Ste. 102
Morena Valley 92557
714-684-6732

Sacramento County Farm Bureau Bulletin
8467 Florin Road, Sacramento 95828
916-383-2841

San Diego County Farm Bureau News
1670 E. Valley Parkway
Escondido 92027
619-745-3023

San Joaquin County Farm Bureau News
P.O. Box 8444, Stockton 95208
209-931-4931

San Luis Obispo County Farm Bureau News
651 Tank Farm Rd., San Luis Obispo 93401
805-543-3654

San Mateo County Farm Bureau News
765 Main Street, Half Moon Bay 94019
415-726-4485

Santa Barbara County Farm Bureau Bulletin
P.O. Box 1846, Buellton 93427
805-688-7479

Santa Clara County Farm Bureau Broadcaster
1368 N. 4th Street, San Jose 95112
408-453-0100

Santa Cruz County Farm Bureau Newsletter
141 Monte Vista Ave., Watsonville 95076
408-724-1356

Shasta County Farm Bureau News
3605 Bechelli Lane, Redding 96001
916-223-2358

Siskiyou County Farm Bureau Newsletter
809 South 4th Street, Yreka 96097
916-842-2364

Small Farm News
c/o University of California Small Farm Center
Davis 95616-8699
916-757-8910

Solano County Farm Bureau Newsletter
2210 Boynton Ave., Ste. E, Fairfield 94533
707-425-8044

Sonoma Marin Farm News
970 Piner Road, Santa Rosa 95403
P.O. Box 6674, Santa Rosa 95406
707-544-5575

Spudman
P.O. Box 1752, Monterey 93940
408-373-7991

Stanislaus County Farm Bureau News
P.O. Box 3070, Modesto 95353
209-522-7278

Sunkist Magazine
P.O. Box 7888, Van Nuys 91409-7888
818-986-4800 Ext. 7454

Sun Diamond Grower
P.O. Box 1727, Stockton 95201
209-467-6000

Tehama County Farm Bureau Newsletter
1130 Metzger Road, Red Bluff 96080
916-527-7882

The Packer
151 Kalmus Drive, Suite 200
Costa Mesa 92626
714-545-8944

TOXICS News
c/o Capitol Reports, 921-11th St., Ste. 701
Sacramento 95814
916-441-4427

Tri Valley Growers Newsletter
P.O. Box 7114, San Francisco 94120-7114
415-445-1600

Trinity County Farm Bureau Newsletter
P.O. Box 1216, Hayfork 96041
916-628-4220

Tulare County Farm Bureau News
P.O. Box 748, Visalia 93279
209-732-8301

Tuolumne County Farm Bureau Newsletter
18971 Hess Ave., Ste. C, Sonora 95370
209-532-5102

Update
California State University-Fresno
School of Agriculture/Sciences &
Technology
Fresno 93740-0115
209-278-2361   FAX 209-278-4849

Ventura County Farm Bureau Broadcaster (Quarterly)
5156 McGrath Street, Ventura 93003
805-656-3552

Ventura County Farm Bureau Newsletter
P.O. Box 3160, Ventura 93006
805-656-3552

Western Grower & Shipper
17620 Fitch St., Irvine 92714
714-863-1000

Water Education Foundation
717 K Street, Ste. 517, Sacramento 95814
916-444-6240   FAX 916-448-5371

Wine Institute Bulletin
425 Market St., Ste. 1000, San Francisco 94105
415-512-0151

Wines & Vines
1800 Lincoln Ave., San Rafael 94901
415-453-9700   FAX 415-453-2517

Yolo County Farm Bureau Newsletter
P.O. Box 1556, Woodland 95695
916-662-6316

PART VI

Oregon & Washington Farm Cooperatives, Related Organizations, and Commodity Commissions

State of Oregon
Oregon Department of Agriculture
635 Capitol Street NE, Salem, OR 97310 503-378-3801 / FAX 503-378-5529

ADMINISTRATIVE OFFICES

Bruce Andrews—Director
Adriana Cardenas—Manager/Commission on
   Agricultural Labor

Phil Ward—Assistant Director, Livestock
   Division/Natural Resources/
   Measurement Standards

Lorna Youngs—Assistant Director, Commodity
   Inspection/Plant Division/
   Laboratory Services/Food & Dairy

Richard Fritz—Assistant Director, Agricultural
   Development
   121 SW. Salmon, Ste. 240
   Portland 97204-2987

FARMER COOPERATIVES

Agripac, Inc.
P.O. Box 5346, Salem, OR 97304
325 Patterson St., NW
Dennis Delaye, President & General
Manager
503-363-9255

Agwest Supply
P.O. Box 47, Rickreall, OR 97371
8870 Rickreall Rd
Larry Crook, General Manager
503-363-2332

Blue Mountain Growers
P.O. Box 156, Milton-Freewater, OR 97862
231 East Broadway
Glen G. Gibbons, Manager
503-938-3391

Condon Grain Growers
P.O. Box 747, Condon, OR 97823
Franklin D. Bauman, Manager
503-384-2491

Coos Grange Supply
1085 South 2nd St., Coos Bay, OR 97420
Richard K. Johnson, Manager
503-267-7051

Del Cur Supply Co-Op
Box AB, Brookings, OR 97415
14397 Hwy. 101 South
Delbert R. Buell, Manager
503-469-5393   FAX 503-469-9222

Diamond Fruit Growers, Inc.
P.O. Box 180, Hood River, OR 97031
11 Third Street
R.K. Girardelli, General Manager
503-386-3111

Farmers Cooperative Creamery
700 N. Hwy 99W, McMinnville, OR 97128
Merle Peters, General Manager
503-472-2157

Farmers Supply Co-Op
514 SW 4th Ave., Ontario, OR 97914
James Sutton, Manager
503-889-5365

**Farmers Union Hay Producers
Marketing Co-op**
Route 1 Box 1960-A, Hermiston, OR 97838
Bob Reuter, Manager
503-567-0208

Full Circle, Inc.—Madras
P.O. Box 49, Madras, OR 97741
116 NW Depot Road
Ted Freeman, Manager
503-475-2222

Full Circle—Tangent
P.O. Box 274, Tangent, OR 97389
99E at Highway 34 Intersection
Howard G. Stahr, Manager
503-926-4404

Grange Cooperative Supply Association
P.O. Box 3637, Central Point, OR 97502
225 South Front Street
James E. Hudson, General Manager
503-664-1261

Branches
Ashland
2nd & A Sts., Ashland, OR 97520
Garfield Lennick, Manager
503-482-2143

Central Point
225 South Front St., Central Point, OR 97502
Norm Rush, Manager
503-664-6691

Medford
2531 South Pacific Highway
Medford, OR 97501
Andy Schofield, Manager
503-772-4730

Hazelnut Growers Bargaining Association
8101 SW Nyberg Road, Suite 201
Tualatin, OR 97062
Mike Klein, Manager
503-692-5932

Hazelnut Growers of Oregon
P.O. Box 626, Cornelius, OR 97113
Larry Holden, General Manager
503-648-4176

Hood River Supply Association
P.O. Box 209, Hood River, OR 97031
1995 12th Street
Pat McAllister, Manager
503-386-2757

Jefferson County Co-Op
P.O. Box Y, Madras, OR 97741
117 N Fifth Street
Errol Schnider, Manager
503-475-2253

Josephine Growers Co-Op Association
P.O. Box 229, Grants Pass, OR 97526
525 NW "F" Street
Michael P. Kerber, General Manager
503-476-7771

Malheur Potato Bargaining Association
P.O. Box 2582, Nyssa, OR 97913
224 West Main
Jack Pressley, President
503-339-3785

Malin Potato Cooperative
P.O. Box 299, Merrill, OR 97633
415 N. Main Street
Don Micka, Manager
503-798-5665

Mid Columbia Producers, Inc.
P.O. Box 344, Moro, OR 97039
2003 First Street
Brian A. Mayer, Manager
503-565-3737

Morrow County Grain Growers
P.O. Box 367, Lexington, OR 97839
Larry Mills, General Manager
503-989-8221

Norpac Foods, Inc.
P.O. Box 458, Stayton, OR 97383
930 West Washington Street
Arthur P. Christiansen, President
503-769-2101   FAX 503-769-5411

Norpac Services, Inc.
P.O. Box 2249, Lake Oswego, OR 97035-0657
4350 SW Galewood
James F. Enger, General Manager
503-635-9311

Northwest Agricultural Co-Op Association
P.O. Box 1, Ontario, OR 97914
920 SE 9th Avenue
F.E. Osborne, President
503-889-3111

Nyssa Cooperative Supply
18 N 2nd Street, Nyssa, OR 97913
George Roth/Barbra McGowen, Co-Managers
503-372-2254

Nyssa-Nampa Beet Growers
P.O. Box 2723, Nyssa, OR 97913
R.T. Rathbone, President
503-372-2904

Oregon Cherry Growers, Inc.
P.O. Box 439, The Dalles, OR 97058
First & Madison Streets
Robert Thompson, General Manager
503-296-5487

Oregon Jersey Co-Op, Inc.
38265 NW Harrington Rd., Cornelius, OR 97113
Pete Jansen, Manager

Oregon Prune Exchange
1840 B Street, Forest Grove, OR 97116
James Lewis, Manager
503-357-6800   FAX 503-357-5048

Oregon Turkey Growers
P.O. Box 5324, Salem, OR 97304
740 Bassett St., NW
Daniel Wallace, General Manager
503-364-3323

Pendleton Grain Growers, Inc.
P.O. Box 1248, Pendleton, OR 97801
1000 SW Dorion
Don Cook, Manager
503-276-7611

Pine-Eagle Farmers Co-Op
P.O. Box 256, Richland, OR 97870
1st Street
Ralph Graven, Manager
503-893-3381

Portland Independent Milk Producers Association
9999 SW Wilshire, Suite 212
Portland, OR 97225
Michael D. Anderson, Manager
503-297-8166

Pratum Co-Op Warehouse
8955 Sunnyview Road, Salem, OR 97305
Robert Kuenzi, Manager
503-364-3353

Rainsweet, Inc.
P.O. Box 13545, Salem, OR 97309-1545
1745 Oxford Street, SE
Mark Gehring, President
503-363-4293

Southern Oregon Sales, Inc.
P.O. Box 1166, 18 Stewart Avenue
Medford, OR 97501
Scott Martinez, General Manager
503-772-6244

Tillamook County Greamery Association
P.O. Box 313, Tillamook, OR 97141
4175 Highway 101 North
D.R. (Pete) Sutton, General Manager
503-842-4481

Tillamook Farmers Co-op Association, Inc.
1920 Main Street N., Tillamook, OR 97141
Dennis Simkins, Manager
503-842-4457

Umatilla Morrow Growers Cooperative
P.O. Box 308, Hermiston, OR 97838
503-567-7700   FAX 503-567-1070

Wallowa County Grain Growers, Inc.
P.O. Box 190, Enterprise, OR 97828
804 Depot Street
Jim Butner, General Manager
503-426-3116

West Valley Farmers
2741 N Hwy. 99W, McMinnville, OR 97128
Sam Graham, General Manager
503-472-6154 or 1-800-422-3178
FAX 503-472-1746

Wilco Farmers, Inc.
P.O. Box 258, Mt. Angel, OR 97362
Rick Jacobson, General Manager
503-845-6122   FAX 503-845-9310

Woodburn Fruit Growers Co-Op Association
P.O. Box 271, Woodburn, OR 97071
960 Young Street
Gary Clark, President
503-981-5311

OREGON AGRICULTURAL ORGANIZATIONS

Agri-Business Council of Oregon
1200 NW Front St., Ste. 290
Portland, OR 97209-2800
Jerry A. Hauck, Executive Vice President
503-221-8756

Agricultural Industries Committee— Portland Chamber of Commerce
1200 NW Front St., Ste. 290
Portland, OR 97209-2800
Kay Shidler, Chairman
503-221-8756

Agricultural Cooperative Council of Oregon
1270 Chemeketa Street N.E., Salem, OR 97301
John McCulley, Executive Secretary
503-370-7019

Agricultural Fiber Association
365 Timothy Lane, Junction City, OR 97448
503-998-1456   FAX 503-998-1522

American Rabbit Breeders—Oregon Chapter
542 Aspen St., Toledo, OR 97391
Carol M. Edwards, President
503-336-2543

Associated Nut Packers
P.O. Box 484, Forest Grove, OR 97116
Wally Reeve, Chairman
503-357-0240

Associated Oregon Industries
P.O. Box 12519, Salem, OR 97309
Richard Butrick, President
503-588-0050   FAX 503-588-0052

Blue Mountain Potato Growers Association
P.O. Box 431, Hermiston, OR 97838
Craig Ward, Secretary
503-566-9099

Central Oregon Hay Growers Association
HC 61, Silver Lake, OR 97638
Everett Solback, President

Central Oregon Potato Growers Association
5352 SW Elbe Drive, Madras, OR 97741
Mark Hagman, President
503-546-4424

Clackamas Broiler Growers Association
25641 S. Schockley Road, Beavercreek, OR 97004
Jeff Bradley, President
503-632-7078

Consumer Programs Committee
P.O. Box 400, Pendleton, OR 97801
Holly Weimer, Chairman
503-384-4231

Eastern Oregon Dairymen's Association
4649 John Day Hwy, Vale, OR 97918
Doug Baker, President
503-473-3006

Eastern Oregon Wool Growers Association
2226 7th Ave. W, Vale, OR 97918
Boyd Perry, President
503-473-2887

**Farm Pac (A political action committee—
active during election years)**
866 Lancaster SE,, Salem, OR 97301
David S. Nelson, Executive Secretary
503-585-1157

Far West Santa Gertrudis Breeders Association
25034 Llewellyn, Corvalis, OR 97333
Mary Jensen, President
503-929-4435

**Fisherman's Marketing Association
(Columbia District)**
320 2nd St., Ste 2B, Eureka, CA 95501
Peter Leipzig, General Manager
707-442-3789

**Grain Transportation Consultants of the
Pacific Northwest (Gratron)**
1200 NW Front St., Ste. 500, Portland, OR 97209
Ray Guimary, Manager
503-228-0133   FAX 503-228-0134

Hood River Grower-Shipper Association
P.O. Box 168, Odell, OR 97044
Thom Nelson, Manager
503-354-2565

Idaho Eastern Onion Committee
5641 Hwy 201, Nyssa, OR 97913
Nobel Morinaka, Chairman
503-372-2889

Independent Trollers of Oregon
Jim Johnson, Coordinator
503-888-5842

Klamath Basin Sheep Producers Association
3328 Vandenberg Rd., Klamath Falls, OR 97603
Ron Hathaway, Secretary
503-883-7131

Klamath Cattlemen's Association
3328 Vandenberg Road, Klamath Falls, OR 97603
Ron Hathaway, Secretary
503-883-7131

Klamath Potato Growers Association
3328 Vandenberg Road
Klamath Falls, OR 97603
Dale Beck, Secretary
503-883-7131

Malheur County Onion Growers Association
5135 Hyline Rd., Oregon Slope
Ontario, OR 97914
Tom Uriu, President
503-262-3922

Malheur Potato Growers Association
710 SW 5th Ave., Ontario, OR 97914
Randy Kameshige, Secretary/Treasurer
503-881-1417

Medford Fruit Growers League
P.O. Box 27, Medford, OR 97501
Peter Naumes, President
503-773-1060

Mid-Willamette Broiler Growers Association
451 Broadmore Ct. NW, Dallas, OR 97335
Nick Aime, President
503-623-5075

Mosier Fruit Growers Association
P.O. Box 302, Mosier, OR 97040
Margaret Roberts, Manager
503-478-3433

National Cattlemen's Association
P.O. Box 3469, Englewood, CO 80155
Earl Peterson, President
303-694-0305

National Farmers Organization
11991 Beyer Lane NE, Woodburn, OR 97071
Ron Hierly, President
503-634-2226

Northwest Chewings and Creeping Red Fescue Association
14446 Riches Road SE, Silverton, OR 97381
Doug Duerst, Treasurer
503-873-8441

Northwest Christmas Tree Association
P.O. Box 3366, Salem, OR 97302
Doug Sager, Secretary/Treasurer
503-364-2942

Northwest Dairymen's Association
635 Elliott Avenue W
Seattle, WA 98119
Richard Low, General Manager
206-284-8120

Northwest Food Processors Association
2300 SW First Ave., Portland 97201-5047
Dave Pahl, President
503-226-2848

Northwest Packers Industrial Relations Association
7100 SW Hampton, Ste. 128, Tigard, OR 97223
Gary Barnes, President
503-684-1727

Nut Growers Society of Oregon and Washington
P.O. Box 23126, Tigard, OR 97223
R. Verne Gingerich, President
503-639-3118

Oregon Agriculture in the Classroom
1200 NW Front Street, Suite 290
Portland, OR 97209-2800
Paul Sunderland, Chairman
503-221-8756

Oregon Alfalfa Seed Growers Association
2690 Twilight Drive, Nyssa, OR 97913
Carl Hill, Chairman
503-881-1419

Oregon Animal Health Council
7200 NE Star Mooring Lane, Newberg, OR 97132
John C. Nyberg, President
503-538-3464

Oregon Association of Conservation Districts
P.O. Box 7275, Salem OR 97303
Harold Lampi, President
503-738-5998

Oregon Association of Nurserymen, Inc.
2780 SE Harrison, Ste. 204
Milwaukie, OR 97222
Clayton W. Hannon, Executive Director
503-653-8733

Oregon Beekeepers Association
19500 N. Hwy 99 W, Dundee, OR 97115
Phyllis Shoemake, Secretary
503-864-2138

Oregon Blueberry Growers Association
39971 Sandner, Scio, OR 97374
Walt Duyck, Vice Chairman
503-769-7669

Oregon Broiler Growers Association
84830 N. Cloverdale, Creswell OR 97426
Spence McGuire, President
503-746-2074

Oregon Caneberry Alliance
P.O. Box 1737, Bandon, OR 97411
Harold Russell, President
503-347-3629

Oregon Cattlemen's Association
Oregon Square, 729 NE Oregon St., Suite 190
Portland, OR 97232
Mick Scott, Executive Director
503-238-7400

Oregon Cattle Women, Inc.
P.O. Box 229, Durkee, OR 97905
Ann D'Ewart, First Vice President
503-877-2340

Oregon Craw Fisherman's Association
23501 S. Trillium Hollow Rd.
Oregon City, OR 97045
Dave Bodenlos, President
503-631-2440

Oregon Dairy Council
Oregon Dairy Center, 10505 SW Barbur Blvd
Portland, OR 97219
Peggy Paul, Director
503-229-5033

Oregon Dairy Farmers Association
Oregon Dairy Center, 10505 SW Barbur Blvd.
Portland, OR 97219
Ed Hemenway, President
503-229-5033

Oregon Dairy Industries
Wiegand Hall, Room 100
Oregon State University, Corvallis, OR 97331
June Daley, Executive Secretary
503-754-5422

Oregon Dairy Women
Oregon Dairy Center, 10505 SW Barbur Blvd.
Portland, OR 97219
Carol Ann Leuthold, President
503-229-5033

Oregon Draft Horse Breeders Association
9101 NW Gass Rd., Carlton 97111
Dave Dunningham, Director
503-852-7571

Oregon Essential Oil Growers League
P.O. Box 3366, Salem, OR 97302
Richard Funke, President
503-364-3346

Oregon Fairs Association
1270 Chemeketa NE, Salem, OR 97301
John McCulley, Executive Secretary
503-370-7019

Oregon Farm Bureau Federation
1701 Liberty St., SE, Salem, OR 97302-5158
Andy Anderson, Administrator
503-399-1701   FAX 503-399-8082

Oregon Feed, Seed and Suppliers Association
1725 NW 24th Ave., Portland, OR 97210
Tillman Stone, President
503-226-2758

Oregon Florists Association
3624 N. Leverman, Portland, OR 97217
Ron Lively, President
503-289-1500

Oregon Forest Industries Council
P.O. Box 12519, Salem, OR 97309
Ward Armstrong, Executive Director
503-371-2942

Oregon Hay Growers Association
HC 61, Silver Lake, OR 97638
Oregon State University
Evertt Solback, President
503-576-2662

Oregon Hop Growers Association
15886 N. Abiqua Rd., Silverton, OR 97381
Gayle Goschie, President
503-633-8686

Oregon Horseman's Association
3525 Garden Ave., Springfield, OR 97478
Edrah Spielman, Secretary
503-746-6564

Oregon Horticultural Society
P.O. Box 1246, McMinnville, OR 97128
W.W. Roberts, Executive Secretary
503-472-7910

Oregon League of Rabbit and Cavy Breeders Association
10405 NE Tillmock St., Portland, OR 97220
Marny Kirkpatrick, Chairman
503-253-7085

Oregon Meadowfoam Growers Association
866 Lancaster Dr., SE, Salem, OR 97302
David S. Nelson, Executive Director
503-585-1157

Oregon Orchardgrass Growers Association
26872 Peoria Rd., Halsey, OR 97348
Larry Warfel, President
503-369-2774

Oregon Pork Producers Council
40417 Fox Valley Road, Lyons, OR 97358
Dave Bonebrake, President
503-859-3356

Oregon Poultry Council
13280 Denbrook Rd., Aurora, OR 97002
Tom Fitzgerald, President
503-678-2156

Oregon Poultry Industries Association
P.O. Box 3003, Portland, OR 97208
John Jenks, President
503-771-1320

Oregon Purebred Sheep Breeders Association
6622 S. Miller Rd., Hubbard, OR 97032
Sandra Ricksager, Secretary
503-651-3268

Oregon Quarter Horse Association
866 Lancaster Dr., SE, Salem, OR 97301
David S. Nelson, Chairman
503-585-1157

Oregon Retail Council
P.O. Box 12519, Salem, OR 97309
James M. Whitty, Director
503-227-5636 or 503-588-0050

Oregon Ryegrass Growers Association
36425 Airport Road, Lebannon, OR 97355
John Polscheider, Vice Chairman
503-451-4201

Oregon Seed Council
866 Lancaster Dr., SE, Salem, OR 97301
David S. Nelson, Executive Secretary
503-585-1157

Oregon Seed League
23865 Peoria Rd., Harrisburg, OR 97446
Lynn Bronson, President
503-995-6079

Oregon Seed Trade Association
1725 NW 24th Ave., Portland, OR 97210
Randy Waldie, Vice Chairman
503-226-2758

Oregon Sheep Advisory Council
Dept. of Animal Science
214 Withy Combe Hall
Oregon State University, Corvallis, OR 97331
Dr. Thomas, Secretary
503-737-1908

Oregon Sheep Growers Association
1270 Chemeketa St., NE, Salem, OR 97301
John McCulley, Director
503-370-7024

Oregon State Agricultural Stabilization & Conservation Service Committee (ASCS)
7620 SW Mohawk, Tualatin, OR 97062
Glen Stonebrink, Executive Director
503-326-2741

Oregon State Fair
2330 17th Street N.E., Salem, OR 97310
Don Hillman, Director
503-378-3247

Oregon State Fur Breeders Association
Route 6, Box 203, Astoria, OR 97103
Carl Salo, Chairman
503-458-5167

Oregon State Grange
1125 SE Madison, Room 102
Portland, OR 97214
Wayne Johnson, Master
503-236-1118

Oregon Thoroughbred Breeders Association
P.O. Box 17248, Portland, OR 97217-0248
Stan Black, Executive Director
503-285-0658

Oregon Tilth Certification Program
Box 218, Tualatin, OR 97062
Yvonne Frost, Project Director
503-692-4877

Oregon Turkey Growers
P.O. Box 5324, Salem, OR 97302
Dan Wallace, General Manager
503-364-3323

Oregon Turkey Improvement Association
P.O. Box 5324, Salem, OR 97304
Bob Ritz, Secretary
503-864-2567

Oregon Water Resources Congress
P.O. Box 3609, Salem, OR 97302
Jan Boettcher, Executive Director
503-363-0121   FAX 503-838-1006

Oregon Wheat Growers League
P.O. Box 400, Pendleton, OR 97801
Scott Hutchinson, Executive Vice President
503-276-7330

Oregon Wine Growers Association
1200 NW Front, Ste. 400, Portland, OR 97209
Betty O'Brien, President
503-228-8336

Oregon Wine Growers Association, Eastern Oregon Region
P.O. Box 320, Broadman, OR 97818
Bob Mueller, President
503-481-6619

Oregon Wine Growers Association, North Willamette Region
4972 Cascade Hwy. SE, Sublimity, OR 97385
Jim Palmquist, President
503-769-9463

Oregon Wine Growers Association Rogue Region
3150 Siskiyou Blvd., Ashland, OR 97520
John Weisinger
503-482-8584

Oregon Wine Growers Association South Willamette Region
24757 Lavell Road, Junction City, OR 97448
Dietor J. Boehm
503-485-3250

Oregon Wine Growers Association, Umpqua Region
P.O. Box 367, Roseburg, OR 97470
Patricia Green, Secretary
503-673-7901

Oregon Women for Agriculture
11525 Bursell Road, Dallas, OR 97338
Loydee Grainger, Chairman
503-838-3250

Oregon Women for Timber
P.O. Box 175, Stayton, OR 97383
Edie Neff, Chairman
503-227-5581

Oregonians for Food and Shelter
567 Union Street NE, Salem, OR 97301
Terry Witt, Executive Director
503-370-8092

South Willamette Broiler Growers Association
84380 N. Cloverdale Road, Creswell, OR 97426
Floyd Henderson, President
503-935-4338

Union County Cattlemen's Association
10507 N. McAllister Road, LaGrande, OR 97805
Gary Farnsworth, Secretary
503-963-1010

United Oregon Horticulture Industry Board
2042 Cordley Hall, Oregon State University
Corvallis, OR 97331
John Wells, Chairman
503-737-3695

Valley Road Blueberry Growers Association
Route 3, Box 252, Cornelius, OR 97113
Walt Duyck, President

Wasco County Fruit & Produce League
3900 Orchard Rd., The Dalles, OR 97058
Ken Bailey, Secretary/Treasurer
503-298-1744

Western Oregon Livestock Association
15151 Feyrer Park Road, Molalla, OR 97038
Steve Coleman, President
503-829-3140

Western Oregon Onion Growers Association
6934 Labish Center Rd. NE, Salem, OR 97305
Terry Bibby, President
503-393-6099

Willamette Dairy Herd Improvement Association
P.O. Box 17399, Salem, OR 97305
Duane Timm, Chairman
503-362-1880

Willamette Filbert Growers
Rt. 5, Box 187, Newberg, OR 97132
R.D. Birkemeier, President
503-538-2401

Willamette Valley Hay Growers
14745 Woodburn Monitor Road NE
Woodburn, OR 97071
Bill Griso, President
503-634-2248

Willamette Valley Potato Growers Association
29244 NW Sauvie Island Rd.
Portland, OR 97231
David Fazio, President
503-621-3566

Willamette Valley Tree Fruit Growers Association
Rt. 1, Box 822, Beaverton, OR 97007
Jack Erhardt, Vice President
503-644-3233

OREGON COMMODITY COMMISSIONS

Chewings Fescue &
Creeping Red Fescue Commission
866 Lancaster Dr. SE, Salem 97301
David S. Nelson, Executive Secretary
503-585-1157   FAX 503-585-1292

Highland Bentgrass Commission
4093 12th Street SE, P.O. Box 3366
Salem, OR 97302
Bryan Ostlund, Executive Secretary
503-364-3346   FAX 503-581-6819

Oregon Alfalfa Seed Commission
200 SW 2nd Ave., Ontario, OR 97914
Mike Derrick, Business Secretary
503-881-1433   FAX 503-881-1444

Oregon Bartlett Pear Commission
813 SW Alder, Ste. 601, Portland, OR 97205
Linda Bailey, Executive Secretary
503-223-8139   FAX 503-294-1428

Oregon Beef Council
729 NE Oregon St., Portland, OR 97232
Mick Scott, Executive Secretary
503-238-7400   FAX 503-238-7444

Oregon Blueberry Commission
247 Commercial NE, Salem, OR 97301
Jan Marie Schroeder, Administrator
503-399-8456   FAX 503-363-0481

Oregon Caneberry Commission
247 Commercial NE, Salem, OR 97301
Jan Marie Schroeder, Administrator
503-399-8456   FAX 503-363-0481

Oregon Clover Commission
Agricultural Development &
Marketing Division
121 SW Salmon St., Ste. 240
Portland, OR 97204-2987
Kim Holland, Administrator
503-229-6734   FAX 503-229-6113

Oregon Dairy Products Commission
Oregon Dairy Center Building
10505 SW Barbur Blvd., Portland, OR 97219
Sheldon Pratt, Executive Secretary
503-229-5033   FAX 503-245-7916

Oregon Dungeness Crab Commission
170 S. 2nd, Ste. 206, Security Bank Bldg.
Coos Bay, OR 97420
Nick Furman, Administrator
503-267-5810   FAX 503-267-5772

Oregon Filbert Commission
P.O. Box 23126, Tigard, OR 97223
Robert Gelhar, Executive Secretary
503-639-3118

Oregon Fryer Commission
11220 SE Stark, Ste. 12, Portland, OR 97216
Paul Rains, Public Relations Manager
503-256-1151

Oregon Grains Commission
1200 NW Front, Ste. 520
Wheat Marketing Center
Portland, OR 97209-2800
Daren Coppock, Administrator
503-229-6574   FAX 503-229-6584

Oregon Hop Commission
1006 Hoffman Road, NE, Salem, OR 97301
Allen Wineland, Executive Secretary
503-588-5769

Oregon Mint Commission
P.O. Box 3366, Salem, OR 97302
Bryan Ostlund, Executive Secretary
503-364-3346   FAX 503-581-6819

Oregon Orchardgrass Seed Producers Commission
1270 Chemeketa NE, Salem, OR 97301
John McCulley, Executive Secretary
503-370-7019   FAX 503-585-1921

Oregon Potato Commission
700 N.E. Multnomah, Ste. 460
Portland, OR 97232-4104
William Wise, Administrator
503-238-7500   FAX 503-239-4763

Oregon Processed Prune & Plum Growers Commission
Agricultural Development & Marketing Division
121 SW Salmon Street, Ste. 240
Portland, OR 97204-2987
Kim Holland, Business Secretary
503-229-6734   FAX 503-229-6113

Oregon Processed Vegetable Commission
1270 Chemeketa NE, Salem, OR 97301
John McCulley, Business Secretary
503-370-7019   FAX 503-585-1921

Oregon Ryegrass Growers Seed Commission
4093 12th Street SE, P.O. Box 3366
Salem, OR 97302
Wally Hunter, Executive Secretary
503-364-3346   FAX 503-581-6819

Oregon Salmon Commission
313 S.W. 2nd St., P.O. Box 1033
Newport, OR 97365
Tom Robinson, Administrator
503-265-2437   FAX 503-265-5241

Oregon Sea Urchin Commission
Agricultural Development & Marketing Division
121 SW Salmon Street, Ste. 240
Portland, OR 97204-2987
Kim Holland, Administrator (acting)
503-229-6734   FAX 503-229-6113

Oregon Sheep Commission
Agricultural Development & Marketing Division
121 SW Salmon Street, Ste. 240
Portland, OR 97204-2987
Kim Holland, Business Secretary
503-229-6734   FAX 503-229-6113

Oregon Strawberry Commission
247 Commercial NE, Salem, OR 97301
Jan Marie Schroeder, Administrator
503-399-8456   FAX 503-363-0481

Oregon Sweet Cherry Commission
Oregon Agri-Services
1701 Liberty SE, Salem, OR 97302
Marshall Coba, Administrator
503-399-1701   FAX 503-399-8082

Oregon Tall Fescue Commission
866 Lancaster Dr., SE, Salem, OR 97301
David S. Nelson, Executive Secretary
503-585-1157   FAX 503-585-1292

Oregon Trawl Commission
P.O. Box 569, Astoria, OR 97103-0569
Joe Easley, Administrator
503-325-3384   FAX 503-325-4416

Oregon Wheat Commission
1200 NW Front Ave., Ste. 520
Portland, OR 97209-2800
Tom Winn, Administrator
503-229-6665   FAX 503-229-6584

Western Oregon Onion Commission
3000 Market St. NE, Ste. 203
Salem, OR 97301
E. Ross, Business Secretary
503-378-7349   FAX 503-370-8994

Wine Advisory Board
635 Capitol NE, Room 101 Agriculture Buiding
Salem, OR 97310-0110
Julianne Allen, Marketing Director
503-373-0004   FAX 503-228-8337

State of Washington
Department of Food and Agriculture

406 General Administration Bldg., AX-41, Olympia, WA 98504-0641 • 206-753-5063
FAX 206-586-6402

ADMINISTRATION DIVISION

C. Alan Pettibone, Director
206-753-5050

Michael V. Schwisow, Deputy Director
206-753-5035

DEPARTMENT ASSISTANT DIRECTORS

Administrative Services
John Frost, Assistant Director
206-586-3454   FAX 206-586-6402

Commodity Inspection
J. Allen Stine, Assistant Director
206-753-7005   FAX 206-586-5257

Consumer and Producer Protection
Mike Willis, Assistant Director
206-753-5065   FAX 206-586-7029

Food Safety and Animal Health
John Daly, Assistant Director
206-753-5043   FAX 206-753-3700

Laboratory Services
Dick Cissell, Assistant Director
206-753-5057

Market Development
Art Scheunemann, Assistant Director
206-753-5046   FAX 206-586-3470

Pesticide Management
Art Losey, Assistant Director
206-753-5062   FAX 206-753-1564

Plant Services
Bill Brookerson, Assistant Director
206-586-5306   FAX 206-586-8574

WASHINGTON COMMODITY COMMISSIONS

Washington Alfalfa Seed Commission
P.O. Box 2966, Pasco, WA 99302
Kenley Maurer, Executive Secretary
509-547-5538

Washington Apple Commission
P.O. Box 18, Wenatchee, WA 98801
Tom Hale, President
509-663-9600   FAX 509-662-5824

Washington Barley Commission
501 Great Western Building, W. 905 Riverside
Spokane, WA 99201
William N. Isgrigg, Administrator
509-456-4400   FAX 509-838-1807

Washington Beef Commission
Denny Building, 2200 6th Avenue, #105
Seattle, WA 98121
Patti Rollinger, Executive Secretary
206-464-7403 / 464-7420

Washington Blueberry Commission
1360 Bow Hill Road, Bow, WA 98232
Dorothy Anderson, Secretary-Treasurer
206-766-6173

Washington Bulb Commission
P.O. Box 303, Mt. Vernon, WA 98273
Richard Nowadnick, Secretary-Treasurer
206-424-1375

Washington Cranberry Commission
P.O. Box 597, Ilwaco, WA 98547
Ardeil McPhail, Chairman
206-642-4938   FAX 206-648-2144

Washington Dairy Products Commission
1107 NE 45th Street, Room 205
Seattle, WA 98105
Doug Simpson, Secretary-Treasurer
206-545-6763   FAX 206-545-6666

Washington Dry Pea & Lentil Commission
5071 Highway 8 West, Moscow, ID 83843
Harold Blain, Administrator
208-882-3023   FAX 208-882-6406

Washington Egg Commission
P.O. Box 1038, Olympia, WA 98507
William J. Walkinshaw, Manager
206-754-4401   FAX 206-754-4414

Washington Fruit Commission
1005 Tieton Drive, Yakima, WA 98902
Ken Severn, President
509-453-4837   FAX 206-453-4880

Washington Fryer Commission
2003 Maple Valley Hwy, Ste. 212
Renton, WA 98055
Pam Williams, Office Manager
206-226-6125   FAX 206-242-2195

Washington Hop Commission
504 North Naches Avenue, #5
Yakima, WA 98901
Ann George, Manager
509-453-4749   FAX 509-457-8561

Washington Mint Commission
P.O. Box 2111, Pasco, WA 99302
Ken Maurer, Executive Secretary
509-547-5538

Washington Potato Commission
108 Interlake Road, Moses Lake, WA 98837
Henry Michael, Administrator
509-765-8845   FAX 509-765-4853

Washington Red Raspberry Commission
1333 Lincoln Street, #182, Bellingham, WA 98226
Anne Seeger, Manager
206-671-1437

Washington Seed Potato Commission
P.O. Box 286, Lynden, WA 98264
Doris Roosma, Secretary-Treasurer
206-354-4670

Washington Strawberry Commission
4430 John Luhr Road, Olympia, WA 98506
Norval Johanson, Manager
206-491-6567

Washington Tree Fruit Research Commission
3630 Lateral B Road, Wapato, WA 98951
David Allan, Secretary-Treasurer
509-877-2065

Washington Wheat Commission
404 Great Western Building, W. 905 Riverside
Spokane, WA 99201
Tom Mick, Administrator
509-456-2481   FAX 509-838-1807

Washington Wine Commission
P.O. Box 61217, Seattle, WA 98121
Simon Siegl, Administrator
206-728-2252   FAX 206-441-3130

FARMER COOPERATIVES

All West Breeders, Select Sires
Box 507, Burlington, WA 98233-0507
Archie Nelson, Manager
206-757-6093   FAX 206-757-7808

Associated Flower Growers, Inc.
Box 53, Spokane, WA 99210
Olive V. Berry, Manager
509-747-8796

Bleyhl Farms Services, Inc.
Box 100, Grandview, WA 98930
Fred Harris, Manager
509-882-1225   FAX 509-882-2355

Blue Chelan, Inc.
Box 789, Chelan, WA 98116
Tony Davey, Manager
509-682-4541   FAX 509-682-4620

Blue Star Growers, Inc.
Box I, Cashmere, WA 98815
Jerry Kenoyer, Manager
509-782-2922   FAX 509-782-3646

CARE
1402, 3rd Ave., #912, Seattle, WA 98101
Peter Bloomquist
206-464-0787

Central Washington Grain Growers
Box 649, Waterville, WA 98858
John Anderson, General Manager
509-745-8551   FAX 509-745-8108

Cheney Grain Growers
Box 309, Cheney, WA 99004
Gorden Young, Manager
509-235-6271   FAX 509-235-2601

Chewelah Grange Supply
P.O. Box 66, Chewelah, WA 99109
Marvin Schmautz
509-935-8332

Chief Tonasket Growers
Box 545, Tonasket, WA 98855
Lee Shamberger, Manager
509-486-2914   FAX 509-486-1101

Chief Wenatchee
Box 1091, Wenatchee, WA 98801
Ted Zacher, President
509-662-5197   FAX 509-662-9415

Clallam Cooperative Association
P.O. Box 608, Sequim, WA 98382
Duane Halter, Manager
206-683-4111   FAX 206-683-2119

Co-Bank
West 601 1st Ave., Box TAF-C2
Spokane, WA 99220-4002
Gary Jurgensen
509-838-9430   FAX 509-838-9237

Colfax Grange Supply Co.
E. 105 Harrison, Colfax, WA 99111
Brian Aafe, Manager
509-397-4324

Columbia County Grain Growers
Box 90, Dayton, WA 99328
Bill Eades, Manager
509-382-2571

Connell Grain Growers, Inc.
Box 220, Connell, WA 99326
Mel Sobolik, Manager
509-234-2641   FAX 509-234-2642

Connell Grange Supply Co.
Box 190, Connell, WA 99326
Kevin Besel, Manager
509-234-9551

Coulee Cooperative
Box 608, Coulee City, WA 99115
Clifford M. Scheib, Manager
509-632-5292

Crisp and Spicy, Inc.
Box 278, Pateros, WA 98846
Gerald Mineard, Manager
509-923-2222   FAX 509-923-2329

Darigold, Inc.
635 Elliott Ave. W., Seattle, WA 98119
Richard Low, Manager
206-284-7220   FAX 206-281-3456

Edwall Chemical Co.
P.O. Box 136, Edwall, WA 99008
R.W. "Dick" Daily, Manager
509-236-2231   FAX 509-236-2217

Fairfield Grain Growers, Inc.
Box 69, Fairfield, WA 99012
Jacqueline R. Tee, Manager
509-283-2124   FAX 209-283-2476

Farm Credit Services
P.O. Box TAX-C5, Spokane, WA 99220
Doyle Cook
509-838-9300   FAX 509-838-9223

Full Circle, Inc.
Rt. 2, Box 95, Moses Lake, WA 98837
Loren Horst, Manager
509-765-5617   FAX 509-765-0777

Graingrowers Warehouse Co.
Box 426, Wilbur, WA 99185
John Anderson, Manager

Grange Insurance Association
200 Cedar St., Seattle, WA 98121
L. Ralph Jones, President
206-448-4911   FAX 206-728-1415

Grange Supply Inc. of Issaquah
145 N.E. Gilman, Issaquah, WA 98027
Dana Dixon, Manager
206-392-6469   FAX 206-392-2348

Grange Supply of Odessa
Box 187, Odessa, WA 99159
Greg Luiten, Manager
509-982-2693   FAX 509-982-2695

Grange Supply of Pullman
NW 355 State Street, Pullman, WA 99163
John N. Johnson, Manager
509-332-2511

Grays Harbor Grange Supply
412 S. Main, Montesano, WA 98563
Roy Rasasen, Manager
206-249-4611   FAX 206-249-4611

Growers Credit Corp.
Box 659, Wenatchee, WA 98807
T. Steve Joy, Manager
509-662-5101   FAX 509-662-7422

Harvest States Cooperatives
811 S.W. Front Ave., Ste. 610
Portland, OR 97204
Donald G. Peterson, President
503-662-5101   FAX 503-662-7422

Inland Empire Pea Growers Assoc.
Box 11126, Spokane, WA 99211
Michael Dunlap, Manager
509-535-2405   FAX 509-535-8837

Johnson Union Warehouse Co.
Rt. 1, Box 170, Colton, WA 99113
Mitchell Payne, Manager
509-229-3315

Lacrosse Grain Growers, Inc.
Box 227, Lacrosse, WA 99143
S.H. Bigsby, Manager
509-549-3535   FAX 509-549-3534

Leavenworth Fruit Co.
P.O. Box 607, Leavenworth, WA 98826
Ron Howerton, Manager
509-548-5823   FAX 509-548-7264

Lincoln Mutual Service #2
Box 129, Reardan, WA 99029
Jim Fuhrman, Manager
509-796-2611   FAX 509-766-3541

Lind Grange Supply Co.
Box 280, Lind, WA 99341
Edwin Fode, Manager
509-677-3471

Magi, Inc.
Box 157, Brewster, WA 98812
George Chapman, Manager
509-689-2511   FAX 509-689-2514

Marcellus Grange Mutual Supply
701 W. 1st, Ritzville, WA 99169
Gordon Aas
509-659-1532

Mid-State Coop.
Box 480, Ellensburg, WA 98926
John "Dick" Potter, Manager
509-925-3525

National Grape Cooperative
P.O. Box 38, Grandview, WA 98930
509-882-1711

Northwest Farm Food Coop
460 Admiral Way, Edmonds, WA 98020
R.N. Lever, Manager
206-778-2106   FAX 206-774-6336

Northwest Wholesale, Inc.
Box 1649, Wenatchee, WA 98801
Jim Standerfard
509-662-2141   FAX 509-663-4540

Oakesdale Grain Growers, Inc.
Box 108, Oakesdale, WA 99158
Chris Meyer, Manager
509-285-4311   FAX 509-285-5930

Odessa Union Warehouse
Box 247, Odessa, WA 99159
Marv Greenwalt, Manager
509-982-2970   FAX 509-982-2970

Palouse Grain Growers
Box 118, Palouse, WA 99161
Bruce A. Baldwin, Manager
509-878-1621   FAX 509-877-1703

Peshastin Fruit Growers Association
Box 378, Peshastin, WA 98847
Richard Fagg, Manager
509-548-7312   FAX 509-486-4786

Peshastin Hi-Up Growers
10100 Mill Road, Peshastin, WA 98847
William P. Burnett, Manager
509-548-7312   FAX 509-782-2513

Plaza Grange Supply
S.36510 Old SR195, Rosalia, WA 99170
Arlin Poulson, Manager
509-523-5511

Pomeroy Grain Growers, Inc.
Box 220, Pomeroy, WA 99347
Roger Dumbeck, Manager
509-843-1694

Pomeroy Grange Supply
P.O. Box 17, Pomeroy, WA 99347
Phil Crawford, Manager
509-843-3693

Pro-Fac Cooperative, Inc.
12112 NW Lower River Road, Vancouver, WA 98660
Albert Fazio, Director
206-693-4216

Puget Sound Cooperative Federation
4201 Roosevelt Way NE, Seattle, WA 98105
Carol DiMarcello, Executive Director
206-632-4559   FAX 206-545-7131

Reardan Grain Growers, Inc.
Box 185, Reardan, WA 99029
Ben Echelbarger, Manager
206-796-4141

Regal Fruit Coop, Inc.
Box 528, Tonasket, WA 98855
Gerald Alumbaugh, Manager
509-486-2158   FAX 509-486-4786

Ritzville Warehouse Co., Inc.
201 E. 1st Avenue, Ritzville, WA 99169
Dave Gordon, Manager
509-659-0130   FAX 509-659-1101

Rockford Grain Growers, Inc.
Box 9, Rockford, WA 99030
Art Grewe, Manager
509-291-5511   FAX 509-291-6161

Rosalia Producers, Inc.
P.O. Box 295, Rosalia, WA 99170
David Peterschick, Manager
509-523-3511   FAX 509-523-5858

St. John Grain Growers, Inc.
Box 208, St. John, WA 99171
Orville J. Mayer, Manager
509-648-3316   FAX 509-648-3315

Seafood Producers Cooperative
2975 Roeder Ave., Bellingham, WA 98225
Berry Lester, Acting Manager
206-733-0120   FAX 206-733-0513

Seattle Fur Exchange
Box 88159, Seattle, WA 98188
Claudia Campbell, Director
206-246-7611   FAX 206-242-2766

Skagit Farm Supply, Inc.
Box 266, Burlington, WA 98233
Ken Kadlec, Manager
206-757-6053   FAX 206-757-2018

Skookum, Inc.
915 N Wenatchee Ave., Box 1987
Wenatchee, WA 98001
509-662-8135   FAX 509-663-3551

Snohomish Cooperative
2nd & Lincoln, Snohomish, WA 98290
Kevin Skolrud
206-568-2104   FAX 206-568-7492

Snokist Growers
P.O. Box 1587, Yakima, WA 98907
Jay Grandy, President
509-453-5631   FAX 509-457-6417

Sprague Grange Supply, Inc.
Box 307, Sprague, WA 99032
Charlie Prentic, Manager
509-257-2271

Touchet Valley Grain Growers
P.O. Box 215, 110 N. Main St.,
Waitsburg, WA 99361
Robert Abbey, Manager
509-337-6633   FAX 509-337-6674

Tree Top, Inc.
Box 248, Selah, WA 98942
Robert Conray, Chief Executive Officer
509-697-7251   FAX 509-697-0421

Uniontown Cooperative Association
Box 127, Uniontown, WA 99179
Eugene Dixon, Manager
509-229-3327

United Grain Growers, Inc.
Box 185, Harrington, WA 99134
Randall Liddell, Manager
509-253-4361   FAX 509-253-4501

Walla Walla Grain Growers
Box 310, Walla Walla, WA 99362
Donald Schmidt, Manager
509-525-6510   FAX 509-525-6050

Washington Asparagus Growers
2810 W. Clearwater Ave., Ste. 202
Kennewick, WA 99336
Mike Harker, Manager
509-783-3094   FAX 509-783-5704

Washington Rural Electric Cooperative Association
Box 2878, Olympia, WA 98507
Aaron Jones, Executive Director

Washtunca Grain Growers, Inc.
Box 735, Washtunca, WA 99371
Wendy Brodahl, Manager
509-646-3223   FAX 509-646-3200

Wenatchee Grange Supply
Box 599, Wenatchee, WA 98801
Jim Fife, Manager
509-662-8188   FAX 509-663-6614

Wenoka Credit Corporation
Box 658, Wenatchee, WA 98801
Gerald Jessup, General Manager
509-663-8585   FAX 509-662-7091

Western Washington Farm Crops Association
1750 S. Burlington Blvd., Burlington, WA 98233
Pete Sword, Manager
206-757-7327   FAX 206-755-0936

Whatcom Farmers Co-op
P.O. Box 611, Lyden, WA 98264
Rich Stipe, Manager
206-354-2108   FAX 206-354-3936

Whitman County Growers
Box 151, Colfax, WA 99111
Robert J. Holmes, Manager
509-397-4381   FAX 509-397-3832

Yakima Cooperative Association, Inc.
2202 South 1st Street, Yakima, WA 98903
509-457-5380   FAX 509-452-2640

Yakima Valley Grape Producers
401 Avenue B, Grandview, WA 98930
Tom McGann, President
509-882-1223   FAX 509-882-1560

AGRICULTURAL ASSOCIATIONS

Amalgamated Growers Association
1750 S. Burlington Blvd., Burlington, WA 98233
James Ferrel, President
206-757-7327

American Dry Pea & Lentil Association
5071 Hwy 8 West, Moscow, ID 83843
Harold Blain, Executive Vice President
208-882-3023   FAX 208-882-6406

Columbia Basin Development League
P.O. Box 715, Othello, WA 99344
Steve Shinn, President
509-488-2623

Far West Fertilizer & Agrichemical Association
P.O. Box 1462, Spokane, WA 99210
Steve Watts, President
509-838-6653

Hop Growers of Washington, Inc.
504 N. Naches Ave., Ste. 5
Yakima, WA 98901
Ann George, Manager
509-453-4749

Inland Empire Agricultural Chemical Association
W. 621 Mallon Ave. Ste. 607, Spokane, WA 99201
Ken Degerness, P.R. Director
509-327-4668   FAX 509-327-4211

Interstate Professional Applicators Association
P.O. Box 1377, Milton, WA 98354
Cindy Deffe, President
206-848-3407

National Farmers Organization
5880 Stratford Road NE, Moses Lake, WA 98837
Rex Chamberlain, President
509-765-1007

Northwest Agricultural Research Foundation
P.O. Box 194, Mt. Vernon, WA 98273
Ken Christianson, President
206-336-9727

Northwest Christmas Tree Association
P.O. Box 3366, Salem, OR 97302
Earl Gingerich, President
503-364-2942

Northwest Dairymen's Association
635 Elliott Ave., W., Seattle, WA 98119
Richard Low, General Manager
206-286-6700   FAX 206-281-3456

Northwest Egg Producers Cooperative Association
P.O. Box 1038, Olympia, WA 98507-0016
Bill Walkinshaw, General Manager
206-754-4401

Northwest Food Processors Association
2300 SW First Avenue, Portland, OR 97201
David A. Pahl, President
503-226-2848

Northwest Horticultural Council
P.O. Box 570, Yakima, WA 98907
Christian Schlect, President
509-453-3193   FAX 509-457-7615

Northwest Quarter Horse Association
Rt. 5, Box 342E, Walla Walla, WA 99362
Rosemary Hof, Secretary
509-525-8308

Northwest Red Raspberry Growers Association
1750 S. Burlington Blvd., Burlington, WA 98233
206-757-3931

Northwest Turfgrass Association
P.O. Box 1367, Olympia, WA 98507
Blair Patrick, Executive Director
206-754-0825

Pacific Coast Oyster Growers Association
4305 Lacey Blvd., SE, Suite 26 & 27
Lacey, WA 98503
Bill Dewey, President
206-459-2828

Pacific Northwest Farmers Union
4017 Albion Street, Boise, ID 83705
Dick Eymann, President
208-383-9570

Pacific Northwest Grain & Feed Association
200 SW Market Street, #1005, Portland, OR 97201
Jonathan Schlueter, Executive Vice President
503-227-0234

Potato Growers of Washington
1807 W. Bonneville St., Pasco, WA 99301
Joe Somolik, Executive Director
509-547-4774   FAX 509-547-0859

Spokane Chamber of Commerce— Ag Bureau
P.O. Box 2147, Spokane, WA 99210
Dennis Fiess, Manager
509-624-1393

Tilth Producers Cooperative
P.O. Box 465, Olympia, WA 98507
Don Heyrick, Editor
206-632-5534

USA Dry Peas & Lentil Council, Inc.
5071 Highway 8 West, Moscow, ID 83843
Tom Bellamore, Marketing Director
208-882-3023   FAX 208-882-6406

Walla Walla Sweet Onion Commission
c/o Bank of the West
P.O. Box 1597, Walla Walla, WA 98362
Wes Colley, Chairman
509-527-3800

Walla Walla Sweet Onion Growers Association
Rt. 1, Box 320, Walla Walla, WA 99362
Craig Christensen, President
509-529-1898

Washington Agricultural Council
P.O. Box 13456, Spokane, WA 99213-3456
Alice Parker, President
509-926-9113

Washington Agriculture & Forestry Education Foundation
Box 13348, Spokane, WA 99213-3348
509-926-9113   FAX 509-926-6993

Washington Asparagus Growers Association
2810 W. Clearwater Ave., Suite 202
Kennewick, WA 99336
Tom Clayton, President
509-783-3094

Washington Association of Apple Growers
P.O. Box 5, Tieton, WA 98947
Ken Volker, President
509-575-4822

Washington Association of Wine Grape Growers
P.O. Box 722, Prosser, WA 99350
Carol Mercer, Executive Secretary
509-786-1000   FAX 509-786-2998

Washington Association of Conservation Districts

Rt. 1, Box 69, St. John, WA 99171
J. Reid Smith, President
509-648-3922

Washington Association of Dry Pea & Lentil Producers

5071 Highway 8 West, Moscow, ID 83843
John Cornwall, President
Harold Blain, Manager
208-882-3023   FAX 208-882-6406

Washington Association of Wheat Growers

109 East 1st, Ritzville, WA 99169
Eric Etzel, Executive Director
509-659-0610

Washington Cattle Feeders Association

P.O. Box 2382, Pasco, WA 99302
Mark Arstein, President
509-547-5538

Washington Cattlemen's Association

P.O. Box 96, Ellensburg, WA 98926
Linda Kelly, Executive Secretary
509-925-9871   FAX 509-925-3004

Washington Certified Grape Nurserymen's Association

Rt. 1, Box 1315, Benton City, WA 99320
Tom C. Judkins, Secretary/Treasurer
509-588-3405

Washington Fish Growers Association

4305 Lacey Blvd., SE, Ste. 26 & 27
Lacey, WA 98503
John Forster, President
206-459-2828

Washington Floricultural Association

12602 - 145th St., East, Puyallup, WA 98374
Dr. Bernard Wesenberg, Executive Director
206-841-4273

Washington Food Processors Council

2300 SW First Ave., Portland, OR 97201-5047
David Klick, Executive Secretary
503-226-2848   FAX 503-227-7374

Washington Friends of Farms and Forests

P.O. Box 7644, Olympia, WA 98507-7644
Duncan Wurm, Executive Director
206-754-1622

Washington Growers Clearinghouse Association

P.O. Box 2207, Wenatchee, WA 98807-2207
Jim Small, President
509-662-6181

Washington Hay Growers Association

Route 1, 842 Road KNW
Quincy, WA 98848
Chris Baumgartner, President
509-787-1339

Washington Mint Growers Association

P.O. Box 2061, Tri Cities, WA 99302
Gary Christensen, President
509-547-5538

Washington Oregon Canning Pear Association

P.O. Box 344, Yakima, WA 98907
Dick McFarland, Secretary/Manager
509-452-8515   FAX 509-452-8528

Washington Pesticide Consultants Association

4702 W. Prasch, Yakima, WA 98908
Ted Nulliner, President
509-966-6662

Washington Pork Producers

Rt. 1, Box 148, Farmington, WA 99128
Scott Cocking, President
208-668-1149

Washington Potato & Onion Association

108 Interlake Road, Moses Lake, WA 98837
Henry Michael, Executive Director
509-765-8845

Washington Resources Council

4322 SW Rocksberry, Seattle, WA 98136
Bill Larson, President
206-935-0756

Washington Rhubarb Growers Association

P.O. Box 887, Sumner, WA 98390
Judith J. Nichols, General Manager
206-863-7333   FAX 206-963-2775

Washington State Beef Commission

2200 6th Ave., Ste. 105 Denny Bldg.
Seattle, WA 98121
Patty Rollinger-Brumbach, Executive Director
206-464-7403   FAX 206-587-5058

Washington State Beekeepers Association

P.O. Box 602, Toppenisk, WA 98948
Alice Bounds, Secreatry
509-865-2279

Washington State Council of Farmer Cooperatives

P.O. Box 7267, Olympia, WA 98507
Karl Kottman, Executive Director
206-357-4616

Washington State Crop Improvement Association
114 N 5th Avenue, Yakima, WA 98902-2642
Keith Pfeifer, Manager
509-248-3240   FAX 509-452-0616

Washington State Dairy Federation
711 S. Capitol Way, Olympia, WA 98501-1231
Mike Watters, President
206-754-4025   FAX 206-943-6987

Washington State Dairy Herd Improvement Association
105 S. Pine St., Burlington, WA 98233-1999
Bob McCauley, General Manager
206-755-0375   FAX 206-755-9580

Washington State Farm Bureau
P.O. Box 2009, Olympia, WA 98507
Darrel Turner, President
206-357-9975

Washington State Farmers Market Association
408 N. Garrison, Olympia, WA 98506
Ray Messegee, President
206-943-2267

Washington State Grange
P.O. Box 1186, Olympia, WA 98507-1186
Robert J. Clark, Master
206-943-9911

Washington State Grape Society
P.O. Box 722, Grandview, WA 98930
Carol Mercer, Executive Secretary
509-786-1000   FAX 509-786-2998

Washington State Holstein Association
20901 Ben Howard Road, Monroe, WA 98272
Eileen Hartzell, Secretary
206-794-7644

Washington State Horticultural Association
Box 136, Wenatchee, WA 98801
Frank DeLong, Executive Vice President
509-548-4728

Washington State Milking Shorthorn Breeders Association
36 Hoctor Road, Goldendale, WA 98620
Roberta Hoctor, Secretary
509-773-4034

Washington State Nursery & Landscape Association
P.O. Box 670, Sumner, WA 98390
Steve McGonigal, Executive Director
206-863-4482

Washington State Vegetable Association
P.O. Box 722, Prosser, WA 99350
Carol Mercer, Managing Director
509-786-1000   FAX 509-786-2998

Washington State Wool Growers Association
5547 Road L, SE, Moses Lake 98837
Dick Appel, President
509-765-1323

Washington Thoroughbred Breeders Association, Inc.
P.O. Box 88258, Seattle, WA 98138
Ralph Vacca, General Manager
206-226-2620   FAX 206-235-1146

Washington Water Resources Association
P.O. Box 593, Yakima, WA 98907-0593
Jeanne Dickman, Executive Secretary
509-575-0026

Washington Wine Institute
1932 First Ave., #510, Seattle 98101
Mike Conway, President
206-441-1892

Washington Women for the Survival of Agriculture—WWSA
P.O. Box 893, Sunnyside, WA 98944
Pam Dufrey
509-837-6787 or 509-837-4428

Wenatchee Valley Traffic Association
P.O. Box 618, Wenatchee, WA 98807
W.W. DeWitt, Secretary/Manager
509-662-2138   FAX 509-662-3127

Western Cascade Fruit Society
4916 52nd Ave., S, Seattle, WA 98118
Dick Tilbury, Secretary
206-723-9009

Western Washington Farm Crop Association
1750 S. Burlington Blvd., Burlington, WA 98233
John Misich, President
206-757-7327   FAX 206-755-0936

Western Washington Horticultural Association
625 Commerce St., Old City Hall, Ste. 310
Tacoma, WA 98402
Mark Christianson, President
206-627-5897

Women Involved in Farming Economics (WIFE)
W. Country Road, Almira, WA 99103
Pat Zimmerman, President
509-639-2257

Yakima Valley Growers & Shippers Association
P.O. Box 1688, Yakima, WA 98907
Keith Matthews, Secretary
509-452-8555   FAX 509-452-8754

PART VII

California agricultural statistical information received from the
State of California, Department of Food and Agriculture, Statistical Review, 1990

CALIFORNIA AGRICULTURAL STATISTICAL SECTION

Sales of farm products in California totaled 18.3 billion in 1990 an increase of 2 percent over the previous year, making this the 43rd consecutive year that the Golden State's diversified products have led the nation, and set a record high for the State.

FIELD CROPS: The value of California's 1990 field crop production was 3 percent above the previous year. Average value of production per acre harvested in 1990 was $659, up from the $620 per acre value in 1989.

FRUIT & NUT CROPS: The total value of California's 1990 fruit and nut crops was up 6 percent from 1989. Grapes continued to lead with 30 percent of the total value.

VEGETABLE CROPS: The total value of California's 1990 vegetable crops was virtually the same as in 1989, estimated to be 3.56 billion. The harvested acreage was 4 percent greater than the previous year.

LIVESTOCK & DAIRY: Cash receipts from farm marketings of meat animals during 1990 totaled over $1.8 billion, up 10 percent from 1989. Receipts from sales of milk and cream during 1990 totaled $2.56 billion, up nearly 5 percent from 1989.

POULTRY: California egg production totaled 7.5 billion eggs during 1990, an increase of 2 percent from 1989. Cash receipts from farm marketings of chicken eggs in 1990 were $433 million, broilers $338 million and turkeys $275 million.

NURSERY AND FLOWER CROPS: The combined nursery and flower industry in California continues to grow. The 1990 total of these two related industries reached $1.9 billion. Most of the increase was recorded on the floriculture side.

ACREAGE AND PRODUCTION BY PRINCIPAL GROUPINGS FOR CALIFORNIA, 1984-90

Acreage of all crops in 1990 totaled 8.1 million acres, down 2 percent from 1989 continuing the decline from the recorded high in 1981. The total tonnage produced in 1990 represents the highest tonnage production recorded due to both fruit and vegetable crops showing record highs.

		Field Crops	Fruit and Nut Crops	Vegetables and Melons	Total
			Acreage Harvested		
Acreage Harvested	1984	5,939,000	1,916,000	996,000	8,851,000
	1985	5,781,000	1,961,000	986,000	8,727,000
	1986	5,290,000	1,971,000	979,000	8,240,000
	1987	5,123,000	1,988,000	1,077,000	8,188,000
	1988	5,289,000	2,005,000	1,107,000	8,400,000
	1989	5,124,000	1,990,000	1,114,000	8,229,000
	1990	4,943,000	1,985,000	1,162,000	8,090,000
			Short Tons		
Production	1984	26,173,000	10,463,000	14,768,000	51,404,000
	1985	26,757,000	11,153,000	14,248,000	52,158,000
	1986	26,719,000	10,757,000	14,456,000	51,933,000
	1987	27,272,000	12,830,000	15,165,000	55,267,000
	1988	25,326,000	13,121,000	15,276,000	53,722,000
	1989	25,187,000	13,226,000	18,161,000	56,573,000
	1990	25,017,000	13,419,000	18,903,000	57,339,000

CALIFORNIA: Number of Farms, Land in Farms, and Size of Farm — 1950-1991

Year	Number of Farms	Land in Farms	Average Size of Farm
		-000 Acres-	-Acres-
1950*	144,000	37,500	260
1955	124,000	39,000	316
1960	108,000	38,800	359
1965	82,000	37,800	461
1970	64,000	36,600	572
1975**	73,000	34,300	470
1980	81,000	33,800	417
1981	83,000	33,600	405
1982	82,000	33,400	407
1983	80,000	33,200	415
1984	78,000	33,000	423
1985	79,000	32,900	416
1986	79,000	32,800	415
1987	83,000	31,900	384
1988	84,000	31,600	376
1989	84,000	31,300	373
1990	85,000	30,800	362
1991	84,000	30,300	361

* Old definition of farm: Places of 10 or more acres that had annual sales of agricultural products of $50 or more and places of less than 10 acres that had annual sales of $250 or more.

** New definition of farm: Places with annual sales of agricultural products of $1,000 or more.

CALIFORNIA FIRSTS: Some 250 crops are recognized in California, including seeds, flowers, and ornamentals. This report contains information for 59 major crops grown on a large commercial scale in California — 14 field crops, 28 fruits and nuts, 15 vegetables, 2 nursery products and cut flowers. In addition, data are shown for 10 livestock and poultry products.

California leads the Nation in the crops shown in the table below. A large number are specialty crops in which the Golden State accounts for most of the U.S. production.

CROP AND LIVESTOCK COMMODITIES IN WHICH CALIFORNIA LEADS THE NATION

Alfalfa Seed	Celery	Kiwifruit	Pistachios
Almonds	Chinchillas	Kumquats	Plums
Apricots	Cowpeas	Ladino Clover Seed	Pomegranates
Artichokes	Crenshaw Melons	Lemons	Prunes
Asparagus	Cut Flowers	Lettuce	Rabbits
Bedding Plants	Dates	Mustard Greens	Raisins
Avocados	Eggs	Nectarines	Safflower
Bermuda Grass Seed	Figs	Nursery Plants	Spinach
Broccoli	Garlic	Olives	Strawberries
Boysenberries	Goat's Milk	Onions	Sudan Grass
Brussels Sprouts	Green Lima Beans	Oriental Vegetables	Table Grapes
Bulbs	Green Onions	Peaches	Tomatoes, Proc.
Cantaloupes	Herbs	Pears, Bartlett	Vegetable & Flower Seeds
Carrots	Greenhouse Vegetables	Persian Melons	Walnuts
Casaba Melons	Honeydew Melons	Persimmons	Wild Rice
Cauliflower	Indoor Plants	Pigeons & Squabs	Wine Grapes

STATE COMMODITY RANKING: California's "Top Twenty" crop and livestock commodities account for over 75 percent of the State's gross farm income. In 1990, dairy products, cattle and calves, and eggs continued to dominate the livestock industry, while grapes, cotton, hay, nursery products, flowers and foliage, lettuce, processing tomatoes, almonds and oranges were the most important crops.

California agriculture is considered one of the most diversified in the world, with no one crop dominating the State's farm economy. This is illustrated by the fact that only one product exceeds 10 percent, and 10 of the top twenty crops individually account for less than 3 percent of the State's total gross farm income. California leads the Nation by a wide margin in the production of fruits and nuts and vegetables.

RANKING AND VALUE, 20 LEADING FARM PRODUCTS, CALIFORNIA, 1989-90

Farm Product	Commodity Ranking		Value a/		Percentage of State Total	
	1989	1990	1989	1990	1989	1990
	Number		1,000 Dollars		Percent	
Milk and Cream	1	1	2,439,057	2,556,002	13.2	13.2
Cattle and Calves	3	2	1,575,944	1,739,859	8.5	9.0
Grapes	2	3	1,692,085	1,499,712	9.2	7.8
Cotton Lint & Seed	4	4	1,032,727	1,182,557	5.6	6.1
Nursery Products	5	5	1,012,250	1,011,412	5.5	5.2
Hay	6	6	852,400	905,463	4.6	4.7
Flowers & Foliage	7	7	723,598	897,562	3.9	4.6
Lettuce	8	8	669,895	682,700	3.6	3.5
Tomatoes, Processing	9	9	586,378	617,001	3.2	3.2
Almonds	10	10	480,930	591,560	2.6	3.1
Oranges	11	11	462,264	562,443	2.5	2.9
Eggs, Chicken	12	12	401,825	433,376	2.2	2.2
Strawberries	13	13	372,201	431,366	2.0	2.2
Chickens	14	14	367,669	343,250	2.0	1.8
Turkeys	15	15	252,472	274,816	1.4	1.4
Tomatoes, Fresh	18	16	239,616	273,258	1.3	1.4
Broccoli	17	17	243,917	244,695	1.3	1.3
Avocados	19	18	207,900	239,400	1.1	1.2
Lemons	24	19	200,671	237,803	1.1	1.2
Walnuts	16	20	245,030	229,270	1.3	1.2

CALIFORNIA'S AGRICULTURAL COMMODITIES:

Commodity ranking, acreage, production, value, crop harvest seasons, and leading producing counties, 1990

Commodity	National Ranking 1/	California's Share of U.S. Production	Harvested Acreage	Production Short Tons (2,000 lbs.)	Value 2/ 000	Rank Among All California Commodities 2/ 1989	Rank Among All California Commodities 2/ 1990	Harvest Season	Leading Counties 10/
	Number	Percent	000 Acres	000 Tons	$1000	Number	Number		
VEGETABLES—TOTAL VALUE—$3,560,880,000									
Asparagus	1	42.5	35.9	52.1	70,833	39	41	Feb. 15-June 30	Imperial, San Joaquin, Monterey
Broccoli	1	91.0	97.5	560.7	244,695	17	17	Continuous	Monterey, Santa Barbara, Imperial, Fresno
Carrots	1	59.5	56.1	869.6	180,184	22	25	Continuous	Kern, Imperial, Fresno, San Luis Obispo
Cauliflower	1	78.4	51.3	307.8	152,929	30	28	Continuous	Monterey, Santa Barbara, Imperial
Celery	1	74.8	24.8	740.6	159,999	27	26	Continuous	Ventura, Monterey, Santa Barbara
Corn, Sweet	3	2.4	20.0	95.0	31,730	49	49	May 1-Dec. 10	Riverside, Ventura, Santa Clara, Contra Costa
Cucumbers for Proc.	3	9.5	4.7	62.5	13,377	59	60	July 1-Sept. 30	San Diego, San Joaquin, Santa Clara, Ventura
Lettuce	1	76.2	162.2	2,798.0	682,700	8	8	Continuous	Monterey, Fresno, Imperial, San Luis Obispo
Melons									
Cantaloupes 4/	1	48.8	83.9	629.3	115,782	26	35	May 15-Nov. 30	Fresno, Imperial, Riverside, Merced
Honeydew	1	75.7	19.0	171.0	54,036	45	43	June 1-Nov. 30	Fresno, Yolo, Imperial, Stanislaus, Sutter
Others 5/	NA	NA	3.5	30.2	8,451	62	62	---	---
Mushrooms, All	2	18.6	0.5	66.5	127,701	31	30	Continuous	Monterey, Santa Clara, San Diego
Onions	1	28.7	39.0	758.0	124,694	33	33	Apr. 1-Oct. 31	Fresno, Imperial, Kern, Los Angeles
Peppers, Chili 4/	2	17.4	4.1	13.6	14,402	60	58	Sept. 15-Dec. 15	Monterey, Santa Clara
Tomatoes									
Fresh Market	1	28.9	38.0	484.5	273,258	18	16	Apr. 15-Dec. 31	Fresno, San Diego, San Joaquin, Merced, Stanislaus
Processing	1	89.9	310.0	9,306.2	617,001	9	9	June 20-Nov. 10	Fresno, Yolo, San Joaquin, Colusa, Solano
Other Vegetables, & Melons, Etc.					689,108				

CALIFORNIA'S AGRICULTURAL COMMODITIES:
Commodity ranking, acreage, production, value, crop harvest seasons, and leading producing counties, 1990

Commodity	National Ranking 1/	California's Share of U.S. Production	Harvested Acreage	Production Short Tons (2,000 lbs.)	Value 2/ 000	Rank Among All California Commodities 2/ 1989	Rank Among All California Commodities 2/ 1990	Harvest Season	Leading Counties 10/
	Number	Percent	000 Acres	000 Tons	$1000	Number	Number		
FRUIT AND NUTS—TOTAL VALUE—$5,060,665,000									
Almonds (Shelled)	1	99.9	411.0	330.0	591,560	10	10	Aug. 1-Oct. 31	Stanislaus, Kern, Merced, Butte, Madera
Apples	3	8.0	31.1	390.0	121,700	34	34	June 15-Oct. 30	Kern, Santa Cruz, Madera, San Joaquin, Tulare
Apricots	1	93.9	16.7	115.0	36,824	48	48	June 1-Aug. 15	Stanislaus, San Joaquin, Kern, San Benito, Merced
Avocados	1	75.5	75.0	105.0	239,400	19	18	Continuous	San Diego, Santa Barbara, Ventura, Riverside
Bushberries 3/									
Boysenberries 4/	1	53.8	0.5	1.8	4,680	65	65	June 1-June 30	Stanislaus
Olallieberries	NA	NA	0.2	1.1	1,760	67	67	June 1-Aug. 30	Santa Cruz
Raspberries 4/	3	2.7	1.7	8.9	29,228	53	51	June 1-July 31	Santa Cruz, Monterey
Cherries, Sweet	3	14.0	10.6	22.0	19,610	52	55	May 20-June 25	San Joaquin, Stanislaus, Santa Clara
Dates	1	99.9	5.0	24.0	20,880	54	54	Oct. 1-Dec. 15	Riverside, Imperial
Figs	1	99.9	16.7	46.0	15,082	56	57	June 10-Sept. 15	Madera, Merced, Fresno
Grapefruit, All	2	19.2	19.2	312.7	30,408	44	39	---	Riverside, San Diego, Kern, Ventura
Desert	---	---	7.6	118.4	34,182	---	---	Nov. 10-June 10	---
Other	---	---	11.6	194.3	46,226	---	---	Mar. 15-Oct. 25	---
Grapes, All	1	91.6	639.0	5,185.0	1,499,712	2	3	---	Fresno, Kern, Tulare, Madera, Napa
Raisin Type	---	---	270.0	2,345.0	546,749	---	---	May 15-Dec. 15	Fresno, Tulare, Kern, Madera
Table Type	---	---	78.0	645.0	276,693	---	---	May 25-Dec. 15	Kern, Tulare, Riverside, Fresno, Madera
Wine Type	---	---	291.0	2,195.0	676,270	---	---	Aug. 5-Dec. 15	Napa, Sonoma, San Joaquin, Madera, Monterey
Kiwifruit	1	100.0	7.3	39.0	14,110	57	59	Sept. 15-Dec. 28	Tulare, Butte, Yuba, Kern, Sutter
Lemons	1	84.4	47.8	596.6	237,803	24	19	Continuous	Ventura, Riverside, San Diego, Kern, Tulare
Nectarines	1	97.0	25.4	211.0	99,940	38	36	June 10-Sept. 5	Fresno, Tulare, Kern, Kings
Olives	1	99.9	30.4	131.0	64,326	41	42	Sept. 25-Mar. 15	Tulare, Tehama, Kern, Butte, Madera
Oranges, All	2	38.6	175.1	2,658.8	562,443	11	11	---	Tulare, Kern, Riverside, Fresno, Ventura
Navel & Misc.	---	---	106.0	1,653.8	358,169	---	---	Oct. 25-May 15	---
Valencia	---	---	69.1	1,005.0	204,274	---	---	Mar. 1-Dec. 1	---
Peaches, All	1	71.8	54.4	792.0	198,122	28	21	---	Fresno, Tulare, Stanislaus, Sutter, Merced
Clingstone	---	100.0	26.9	506.0	102,078	---	---	July 15-Sept. 15	---
Freestone	---	47.9	27.5	286.0	96,044	---	---	May 10-Sept. 15	---
Pears, All	2	34.4	23.3	332.0	83,248	37	38	July 5-Oct. 5	Sacramento, Lake, Mendocino, Solano
Pecans	8	1.4	2.6	1.4	3,500	66	66	Sept. 1-Nov. 30	Tulare, Fresno
Pistachios	1	100.0	49.8	59.0	127,440	40	31	Sept. 15-Dec. 10	Kern, Madera, Kings, Tulare
Plums	1	82.3	41.7	222.0	133,804	35	29	May 25-Sept. 20	Fresno, Tulare, Kern, Kings
Prunes, Dried Basis	1	100.0	78.0	147.0	125,097	29	32	Sept. 15-Nov. 10	Sutter, Yuba, Tehama, Glenn, Butte

CALIFORNIA'S AGRICULTURAL COMMODITIES: Fruit and Nuts Continued from Preceding Page

Commodity	National Ranking 1/	California's Share of U.S. Production	Production		Value 2/	Rank Among All California Commodities 2/		Harvest Season	Leading Counties 10/
			Harvested Acreage	Short Tons (2,000 lbs.)		1989	1990		
	Number	Percent	000 Acres	000 Tons	$1000	Number			
Strawberries 3/	1	78.7	20.0	495.0	431,366	13	13	Feb. 20-Nov. 15	Monterey, Ventura, Santa Barbara, Santa Cruz, Orange
Fresh Market	1	77.7	---	336.8	352,241	---	---	---	
Processing	1	81.1	---	158.2	79,125	---	---	---	
Tangerines, Mandarins, Tangelos, & Tangors	2	23.4	7.3	60.0	29,282	51	50	Nov. 1-Apr.30	Riverside, Tulare
Walnuts 4/	1	99.0	181.0	227.0	229,270	16	20	Sept. 5-Nov. 10	Tulare, San Joaquin, Stanislaus, Butte, Sutter
Other Fruit and Nuts					60,070				

CALIFORNIA'S AGRICULTURAL COMMODITIES:

Commodity ranking, acreage, production, value, crop harvest seasons, and leading producing counties, 1990

Commodity	National Ranking 1/ Number	California's Share of U.S. Production Percent	Harvested Acreage 000 Acres	Production Short Tons (2,000 lbs.) 000 Tons	Value 2/ 000 $1000	Rank Among All California Commodities 2/ 1989 Number	Rank Among All California Commodities 2/ 1990 Number	Harvest Season	Leading Counties 10/
FIELD AND SEED CROPS—TOTAL VALUE—$3,257,224,000									
Alfalfa Seed 4/	1	37.7	71.0	17.5	50,494	46	44	Aug.15-Oct. 15	Fresno, Kings, Imperial
Barley	8	2.4	200.0	240.0	26,500	47	52	May 15-Oct. 1	Kings, Tulare, Siskiyou, Kern, Modoc
Beans, Dry	6	9.6	168.0	155.4	94,483	32	37	Aug. 20-Nov. 15	Stanislaus, San Joaquin, Tulare, Fresno, Kern
Corn for Grain	23	0.3	160.0	716.8	78,080	36	40	Sept. 1-Dec. 1	San Joaquin, Solano, Sacramento, Tulare, Merced
Cotton	2	---	---	---	1,182,557	4	4	---	Fresno, Kern, Kings, Tulare, Merced
Lint	2	18.0	1,115.5	669.9	1,021,281	---	---	Oct. 1-Jan. 1	---
Seed	2	17.9	---	1,089.7	161,276	---	---	---	---
Hay, Alfalfa & Other	2	5.7	1,630.0	8,307.0	905,463	6	6	Mar. 1-Nov. 5	Imperial, Tulare, Kern, Fresno, Merced
Oats	16	0.8	40.0	48.0	4,800	64	64	June 15-Oct. 1	Siskiyou, San Joaquin, Merced, Santa Clara, Solano
Potatoes	7	4.5	50.0	889.2	183,580	21	24	Continuous	Kern, Riverside, Siskiyou, Modoc
Rice 11/	2	18.9	385.0	1,463.0	190,190	20	22	Sept. 1-Nov. 30	Butte, Colusa, Glenn, Sutter, Yuba
Safflower 4/ 6/	1	76.6	116.6	142.3	37,150	43	47	July 1-Sept. 15	Kings, Yolo, San Joaquin, Sutter, Fresno
Sugar Beets 7/	3	15.8	167.0	4,359.0	184,386	25	23	Apr. 1-Dec. 10	Imperial, San Joaquin, Fresno, Solano, Kern
Sweet potatoes	3	11.5	8.3	72.7	24,265	50	53	July 15-Nov. 15	Merced, Fresno, Stanislaus
Wheat	18	2.2	614.0	1,437.2	157,618	23	27	May 20-Sept. 1	Fresno, Imperial, Kings, San Joaquin, Tulare
Other Field Crops					137,658	---	---		
NURSERY AND FLOWER CROPS—TOTAL VALUE—$1,908,974,000									
Nursery Products 4/ 6/ 9/	1	24.5	---	---	1,011,412	5	5	Continuous	San Diego, Los Angeles, Orange, San Mateo, Ventura
Flowers and Foliage 4/ 6/ 8/	1	24.5	---	---	897,562	7	7	Continuous	San Diego, Monterey, San Mateo, Santa Barbara, Santa Cruz

CALIFORNIA'S AGRICULTURAL COMMODITIES:
Commodity ranking, acreage, production, value, crop harvest seasons, and leading producing counties, 1990

Commodity	National Ranking 1/	California's Share of U.S. Production	Marketings 1/	Cash Receipts 2/	Rank Among All California Commodities 2/		Leading Counties 10/
					1989	1990	
	Number	Percent	000 Pounds	$1,000	Number		
LIVESTOCK, POULTRY, APIARY AND FISH—TOTAL VALUE—$5,515,159,000							
Cattle and Calves	6	5.0	2,661,120	1,739,859	3	2	Imperial, Tulare, Fresno San Bernardino
Chickens, All	7	4.5	1,191,280	343,250	14	14	Merced, Stanislaus
Broilers and Fryers	9	4.3	1,109,280	338,330	---	---	
Other	3	8.4	82,000	4,920	---	---	
			(Millions of eggs)				
Eggs, Chicken	1	11.0	7,472	433,376	12	12	Riverside, San Diego, San Bernardino, Stanislaus, San Joaquin
Hogs and Pigs	26	0.3	65,676	38,486	55	46	Tulare, Merced, Stanislaus
Honey	2	10.3	20,160	10,886	63	61	Riverside, Tulare, Fresno, Imperial, Kings
Milk and Cream	2	14.3	20,908,000	2,556,002	1	1	Tulare, San Bernardino, Riverside, Merced, Stanislaus
Sheep and Lambs	2	10.0	87,706	44,583	42	45	Kern, Solano, Imperial, Fresno, Merced
Turkeys	3	12,0	723,200	274,816	15	15	Fresno, Stanislaus, Kings, Merced, Tulare
Wool	3	8.7	7,646	6,270	61	63	Kern, Fresno, Solano, Merced
Aquaculture		----	---	17,857	58	56	
Other Livestock & Poultry				49,775			

1/ Based on quantity produced for crops and on quantity marketed for livestock and poultry products.
2/ Based on value of quantity harvested for crops, value of quantity marketed for livestock and value of quantity produced for poultry products.
3/ In past bulletins, berries have been listed and summarized in the vegetable tables and totals. Starting in this publication we have revised the data to show berries in the fruit tables and totals.
4/ Share of U.S. production based on 1987 Census of Agriculture.
5/ From 1990 casabas, crenshaws, and persians were combined into "Others."
6/ Extracted from Agricultural Commissioners' Annual Crop Reports.
7/ The 1990 price and value are based on the 1989 California average price.
8/ Includes cut flowers, potted plants, foliage plants, bedding plants and indoor decoratives.
9/ Includes trees, shrubs, vines, bulbs, turf, etc., not included in flowers and foliage category.
10/ Based on values published in the Annual County Agricultural Commissioners' Reports.
11/ The 1990 price and value are based on U.S. average price.

Principal Crops: Average Value, California, 1981-90

1981	1982	1983	1984	1985	1986	1987	1988	1989	1990
Field Crops (billion dollars)									
$3,598	$3,142	$2,663	$3,129	$2,912	$2,337	$2,893	$2,995	$3,178	$3,257
Fruit and Nut Crops									
3.134	3,354	2,688	3,127	3,325	3,685	4,121	4,589	4,786	5,061
Vegetables and Melons									
2.317	2,543	2,650	2,858	2,711	2,882	3,229	3,281	3,555	3,561
Total Average Value of Crops									
9.049	9,039	8,001	9,114	8,948	8,904	10,243	10,865	11,519	11,879

CALIFORNIA'S LEADING AGRICULTURAL COUNTIES*
BY TOTAL VALUE OF PRODUCTION — 1990
VALUE OF AGRICULTURAL PRODUCTS FOR 1990
(Timber not included)

Rank 1990	Rank 1989	County	Value of Production -000 Dollars-	Leading Crops
1	1	Fresno	2,938,504	Grapes, Cotton Lint, Proc. Tomatoes, Turkeys, Milk
2	2	Tulare	2,163,284	Milk, Oranges, Grapes, Cattle & Calves, Cotton Lint
3	3	Kern	1,836,224	Cotton, Grapes, Carrots, Almonds, Oranges, Potatoes
4	4	Monterey	1,397,599	Lettuce, Strawberries, Broccoli, Floral & Nursery
5	5	Riverside	1,137,174	Milk, Grapes, Eggs, Oranges, Grapefruit, Floral & Nursery
6	6	Merced	1,099,085	Milk, Chickens, Almonds, Cotton, Alfalfa Hay, Cattle & Calves
7	7	Stanislaus	1,038,356	Milk, Chickens, Almonds, Cattle & Calves, Chicken Eggs
8	8	Imperial	1,016,811	Cattle & Calves, Alfalfa Hay, Cantaloupes, Lettuce, Carrots
9	11	San Diego	934,029	Floral & Nursery, Avocados, Chicken Eggs, Oranges
10	9	San Joaquin	874,620	Milk, Grapes, Proc. Tomatoes, Almonds, Floral & Nursery
11	10	Ventura	851,541	Lemons, Floral & Nursery, Strawberries, Celery, Oranges
12	12	Kings	767,957	Cotton Lint, Milk, Cattle & Calves, Cottonseed, Turkeys
13	13	San Bernardino	663,696	Milk, Cattle & Calves, Chicken Eggs, Floral & Nursery
14	14	Santa Barbara	515,590	Floral & Nursery, Strawberries, Avocados, Cattle & Calves
15	15	Madera	514,797	Grapes, Almonds, Cotton, Milk, Pistachios, Turkeys
16	17	Sonoma	290,698	Grapes, Milk, Floral & Nursery, Cattle & Calves, Chicken Eggs
17	16	Los Angeles	274,029	Floral & Nursery, Eggs, Chickens, Onions, Alfalfa Hay
18	18	San Luis Obispo	272,687	Lettuce, Floral & Nursery, Grapes, Cattle & Calves
19	19	Orange	256,754	Floral & Nursery, Strawberries, Oranges, Fresh Tomatoes
20	21	Yolo	242,036	Proc. Tomatoes, Alfalfa Hay, Wheat, Rice, Honeydew Melons
21	22	Butte	239,232	Rice & Seed, Almonds, Walnuts, Prunes, Kiwifruit, Peaches
22	24	Sacramento	236,357	Milk, Pears, Cattle & Calves, Floral & Nursery, Field Corn
23	20	Sutter	217,400	Rice & Seed, Prunes, Peaches, Proc. Tomatoes, Walnuts
24	23	Colusa	207,720	Rice & Seed, Proc. Tomatoes, Almonds, Vine Seeds
25	26	San Mateo	206,879	Floral & Nursery, Artichokes, Brussels Sprouts, Cattle & Calves
26	28	Santa Cruz	192,558	Strawberries, Floral & Nursery, Lettuce, Raspberries, Apples
27	25	Glenn	192,016	Rice & Seed, Milk, Almonds, Prunes, Cattle & Calves
28	27	Solano	175,230	Proc. Tomatoes, Sugar Beets, Nursery Stock, Cattle & Calves
29	31	Siskiyou	152,151	Cattle & Calves, Alfalfa, Potatoes & Seed, Other Hay
30	29	Napa	147,257	Grapes, Cattle & Calves, Floral & Nursery, Milk, All Hay
31	30	Santa Clara	141,737	Floral & Nursery, Mushrooms, Cattle & Calves, Bell Peppers
32	32	San Benito	129,119	Floral & Nursery Crops, Cattle & Calves, Lettuce, Bell Peppers
33	34	Tehama	90,571	Walnuts, Prunes, Cattle & Calves, Olives, Almonds, Milk
34	33	Yuba	89,296	Prunes, Rice, Peaches, Cattle & Calves, Walnuts, Milk
35	36	Modoc	69,070	Cattle & Calves, Potatoes & Seed, Alfalfa Hay, Irrigated Pasture

*Excluding Alpine County — No Agricultural Commissioner

SOURCE: California Agricultural Commissioners' Annual Crop Reports.

TOP 20 STATES IN 1990 CASH FARM RECEIPTS

State	Rank						Cash Receipts in Billions
	1990	1989	1988	1987	1986	1985	
California	1	1	1	1	1	1	$18.3
Texas	2	2	2	2	3	3	11.8
Iowa	3	3	3	3	2	2	10.3
Nebraska	4	4	4	4	4	4	8.8
Illinois	5	5	6	5	5	5	8.0
Minnesota	6	6	7	6	6	6	7.0
Kansas	7	7	5	7	7	7	7.0
Wisconsin	8	9	9	8	8	8	5.7
Florida	9	8	8	9	9	10	5.7
Indiana	10	11	11	10	10	9	4.9
North Carolina	11	10	10	11	11	11	4.9
Arkansas	12	12	12	17	17	14	4.3
Colorado	13	13	14	14	16	15	4.2
Ohio	14	16	15	13	12	12	4.2
Missouri	15	14	13	12	13	13	3.9
Georgia	16	15	16	16	14	16	3.8
Washington	17	17	18	18	18	20	3.8
Pennsylvania	18	19	19	15	15	17	3.8
Oklahoma	19	18	17	19	/	/	3.6
South Dakota	20	20	20	20	/	/	3.3

TOTAL 1990 U.S. TOTAL CASH RECEIPTS $169.3

SOURCE: USDA, Economic Research Service, Economic Indicators of the Farm Sector.

CALIFORNIA: Market value of farm real estate per acre, by region, 1982-91

Land Use and Region	1982	1983	1984	1985	1986	1987	1988	1989	1990	1991
					---Dollars---					
IRRIGATED										
Truck and Vegetables										
North & East Central	---	2,470	2,430	2,070	1,900	1,900	2,250	---	---	---
Central Coast	6,380	6,410	6,400	5,900	6,300	7,000	7,200	7,600	8,100	8,500
Sacramento Valley	3,650	3,660	3,400	2,800	2,500	2,200	2,300	2,350	2,600	2,850
San Joaquin Valley	4,570	4,660	4,500	3,500	2,950	2,900	3,050	3,300	3,600	3,800
So. California	6,600	6,800	7,100	6,000	6,200	6,400	6,300	6,600	6,800	7,500
Cotton										
San Joaquin Valley	---	---	---	2,900	2,400	2,250	2,350	2,500	2,750	2,800
So. California	---	---	---	2,800	2,500	2,500	2,400	2,300	2,300	2,500
Rice										
Sacramento Valley	---	---	---	1,800	1,700	1,500	1,600	1,600	1,800	2,000
San Joaquin Valley	---	---	---	1,950	1,800	1,600	1,850	1,950	2,100	2,200
Extensive Field Crops b/										
North & East Central	1,700	1,780	1,700	1,530	1,600	1,400	1,300	1,400	1,200	1,400
Central Coast	3,100	2,760	2,800	2,750	2,700	2,600	2,600	2,650	2,800	3,300
Sacramento Valley	2,850	2,700	2,750	2,400	2,150	1,900	1,900	2,000	2,000	2,300
San Joaquin Valley	3,640	3,750	3,500	3,000	2,600	2,400	2,650	2,900	3,000	3,100
So. California	3,460	3,640	3,700	3,200	3,200	3,200	3,300	3,500	3,700	4,000
Pasture										
North & East Central	1,400	1,500	1,370	1,340	1,400	1,350	1,350	1,450	1,450	1,550
Central Coast	2,200	2,300	2,300	2,400	2,700	2,650	2,850	2,850	2,800	3,200
Sacramento Valley	2,060	1,960	1,950	1,800	1,600	1,400	1,650	1,800	1,800	1,900
San Joaquin Valley	2,420	2,530	2,400	2,300	2,000	2,050	2,300	2,350	2,500	2,700
So. California	---	---	---	2,700	3,000	3,200	3,300	---	---	---
NONIRRIGATED										
Cropland										
North & East Central	850	870	840	820	900	900	800	800	900	1,000
Central Coast	1,500	1,490	1,550	1,500	1,250	1,500	1,600	1,600	1,650	1,950
Sacramento Valley	1,400	1,470	1,490	1,100	900	800	800	900	950	1,100
San Joaquin Valley	1,710	1,600	1,560	1,300	1,100	900	1,100	1,300	1,300	1,350
So. California	---	---	---	2,200	2,400	2,800	2,750	3,200	---	---
Pasture										
North & East Central	700	700	700	750	770	700	750	800	850	850
Central Coast	990	1,000	1,150	1,100	1,150	1,200	1,200	1,300	1,300	1,450
Sacramento Valley	1,120	1,030	1,100	1,000	900	750	700	800	850	900
San Joaquin Valley	1,310	1,210	1,206	1,050	900	850	900	1,050	1,050	1,100
Rangeland c/										
North & East Central	450	460	540	500	500	500	450	450	450	500
Central Coast	700	650	740	800	850	900	900	900	950	1,000
Sacramento Valley	650	660	650	650	650	550	500	550	550	550
San Joaquin Valley	700	700	750	700	650	600	600	700	650	600

a/ Excludes value of farm buildings.

b/ Includes land used for barley, beans, corn, and sorghum. Beginning 1985 includes land used for alfalfa, wheat, barley sugar beets, beans, and corn.

c/ Unimproved

CALIFORNIA: Market value per acre of orchards, vineyards, and groves, by region, 1982-1991*

Land Use and Region	Year									
	1982	1983	1984	1985	1986	1987	1988	1989	1990	1991
	---Dollars---									
ORCHARD										
Almonds										
Sacramento Valley	5,940	7,080	6,200	4,900	4,300	4,500	4,800	4,900	4,900	5,000
San Joaquin Valley	8,570	7,390	6,700	5,900	5,300	5,200	5,400	5,800	6,200	6,400
English Walnuts										
Central Coast	8,500	8,330	---	---	6,700	6,300	5,900	6,000	6,700	7,000
Sacramento Valley	8,750	7,990	7,500	6,200	5,400	5,100	5,200	5,600	6,000	6,600
San Joaquin Valley	8,780	8,380	7,900	6,200	5,500	5,500	6,000	6,100	6,500	6,700
Pistachios										
San Joaquin Valley	---	---	---	---	8,700	8,400	8,400	8,400	8,800	9,400
Apples										
Central Coast	9,600	---	---	---	9,950	10,200	10,000	---	---	---
San Joaquin Valley	---	---	---	5,810	6,300	7,000	6,500	6,600	6,900	7,100
Apricots										
Central Coast	---	---	---	---	6,300	6,800	6,700	---	7,500	7,600
Sacramento Valley	---	---	---	---	4,200	4,400	4,300	---	5,300	5,300
San Joaquin Valley	7,270	7,340	7,000	5,200	4,900	5,000	5,200	5,800	6,300	6,400
Avocados										
San Joaquin Valley	---	---	---	---	---	---	---	---	7,000	7,100
So. California	17,720	17,030	17,200	14,500	14,500	13,500	15,500	17,000	17,500	19,500
Cherries										
San Joaquin Valley	---	---	---	---	6,850	6,600	7,500	7,800	8,000	8,000
Nectarines										
San Joaquin Valley	8,970	8,500	7,470	6,300	5,600	6,000	6,000	6,300	6,700	7,000
Olives										
San Joaquin Valley	5,800	---	---	5,230	5,700	5,900	6,200	6,250	6,250	6,300
Peaches										
Sacramento Valley	5,940	5,590	5,600	4,840	4,650	4,400	4,550	5,200	6,000	6,600
San Joaquin Valley	8,570	7,410	7,200	6,100	5,600	5,500	5,550	6,100	6,800	7,200
Pears										
Central Coast	7,700	7,440	5,400	---	5,256	5,200	---	---	---	---
Sacramento Valley	5,280	5,350	4,800	3,600	4,400	4,300	4,400	4,800	5,000	5,800
San Joaquin Valley	---	---	---	---	5,150	5,100	5,300	---	6,200	6,400
Plums										
San Joaquin Valley	9,770	8,770	8,100	6,300	5,800	6,000	5,600	6,300	6,400	6,700
Prunes										
Central Coast	8,300	8,200	8,070	---	---	6,100	---	---	---	---
Sacramento Valley	5,930	5,690	5,400	4,900	4,400	4,200	4,250	4,600	5,000	5,400
San Joaquin Valley	7,770	---	---	4,860	5,200	5,600	5,500	6,000	6,200	6,200
CITRUS										
Grapefruit										
So. California	9,870	9,560	9,200	10,000	11,000	9,600	10,000	10,900	10,900	12,400
Lemons										
San Joaquin Valley	6,440	6,850	6,700	6,000	7,300	7,000	7,250	7,500	7,800	7,700
So. California	14,110	13,860	13,500	13,500	13,400	13,000	13,400	15,000	16,500	18,000

Excluding nonbearing acreage and farm buildings.

CALIFORNIA: Market value per acre of orchards, vineyards, and groves, by region, 1982-1991*

Land Use and Region	1982	1983	1984	1985	1986	1987	1988	1989	1990	1991
					---Dollars---					
Navel Oranges										
San Joaquin Valley	7,410	7,510	8,070	8,000	8,250	8,000	8,100	8,500	9,000	8,500
So. California	11,400	10,100	11,180	11,810	13,400	11,900	12,900	14,300	14,500	18,000
Valencia Oranges										
San Joaquin Valley	7,260	7,830	7,900	8,100	8,400	8,400	8,100	8,600	9,100	8,600
So. California	12,030	11,110	12,000	12,000	13,000	13,000	14,400	16,000	17,500	18,000
Tangerines										
San Joaquin Valley	6,530	6,670	7,820	---	7,000	7,200	7,200	7,800	8,200	10,500
VINEYARDS										
Raisin Varieties										
San Joaquin Valley	10,840	9,460	6,580	4,520	4,000	4,300	4,850	5,300	5,800	5,900
Table Varieties										
San Joaquin Valley	9,560	9,920	7,810	5,550	4,850	5,000	5,400	5,900	6,100	6,300
Wine Varieties										
Central Coast	15,840	15,230	16,640	14,790	15,400	16,000	16,400	19,000	21,500	22,600
San Joaquin Valley	9,770	8,060	6,380	4,680	4,000	4,200	4,800	5,200	5,600	5,400
Kiwifruit										
Sacramento Valley	---	---	---	---	---	12,600	11,300	12,000	10,200	8,200
San Joaquin Valley	---	---	---	---	10,600	10,600	9,100	9.,400	8,500	7,300

*Excluding nonbearing acreage and farm buildings.

CROP REPORTING DISTRICTS

- (33) North and East Central
- (40) Central Coast
- (50) Sacramento Valley
- (51) San Joaquin Valley
- (80) Southern

PRICES RECEIVED FOR FIELD CROPS, CALIFORNIA*

Year and Month	Wheat per cwt.	Oats per cwt.	Barley per cwt.	Dry Beans per cwt.	Potatoes per cwt.	All Hay per ton	Alfalfa Hay per ton	Upland Cotton per lb.
				---Dollars---				
1990 January	6.18	5.09	5.27	35.00	12.80	107.00	110.00	.668
February	5.58	5.59	5.69	35.00	12.30	107.00	109.00	.700
March	6.23	5.06	5.40	35.00	15.60	108.00	109.00	.738
April	6.42	5.03	5.63	34.00	11.00	121.00	123.00	.757
May	6.10	4.88	5.67	34.00	12.70	119.00	124.00	.812
June	5.80	5.03	5.75	35.00	9.75	109.00	113.00	.735
July	5.83	5.00	5.67	34.00	10.00	102.00	104.00	.739
August	5.22	5.00	5.15	33.50	12.70	101.00	103.00	.775
September	4.82	5.06	4.81	31.00	6.70	103.00	104.00	.758
October	4.82	5.09	4.69	30.50	6.50	106.00	108.00	.742
November	4.55	5.13	5.04	30.00	8.80	107.00	109.00	.747
December	4.58	5.06	4.85	30.00	11.60	104.00	105.00	.776
1990 Average	5.48	5.00	5.52	30.40	10.40	109.00	110.00	.757
1989 Average	6.37	5.19	5.54	34.80	11.40	100.00	102.00	.718
1988 Average	6.37	7.66	5.73	36.20	9.15	94.00	---	.647

Marketing year average.

PRICES RECEIVED FOR FRUIT CROPS, CALIFORNIA (Grower Return Basis)*

Year and Month	Apples Fresh per lb.	Peaches Fresh per lb.	All Pears Fresh per lb.	Straw-berries per cwt.	Navel Oranges Fr. per ctn.	Valencia Oranges Fr. per ctn.	Grapefruit Fresh per ctn.	Lemons Fresh per ctn.	Tangerines Fresh per ctn.
				---Dollars---					
1990 January	.252	---	---	150.00	4.84	---	6.58	8.27	11.51
February	.293	---	---	115.00	4.74	---	6.46	9.22	12.06
March	.289	---	---	115.00	4.44	5.71	7.06	10.07	7.76
April	---	---	---	50.00	4.24	5.61	7.34	10.27	7.76
May	---	.265	---	35.00	5.04	6.76	8.02	10.57	8.01
June	---	.241	---	45.00	5.29	6.01	7.73	11.17	---
July	---	.242	.205	40.00	---	5.11	5.93	11.52	---
August	.236	.177	.135	50.00	---	5.01	4.44	9.62	---
September	.280	.156	.099	55.00	---	4.26	3.10	8.99	---
October	.236	---	.088	75.00	---	4.66	1.89	11.29	---
November	.322	---	---	125.00	7.39	4.01	2.94	8.54	13.21
December	.366	---	---	130.00	6.24	---	4.67	6.94	10.27
1990 Average	.291	.217	.126	52.30	4.89	5.41	6.75	10.62	10.76
1989 Average	.262	.196	.136	49.30	4.68	5.68	4.64	9.20	9.33
1988 Average	.320	.198	.124	52.00	4.79	5.69	4.45	8.16	10.34

Most citrus and apple averages are based on marketing year and include some prices from previous year; peaches, pears and Valencia oranges are on a calendar year.

PRICES RECEIVED FOR LIVESTOCK AND LIVESTOCK PRODUCTS, CALIFORNIA

Year and Month	All Beef Cattle per cwt.	Beef Cows per cwt.	Steers & Heifers per cwt.	Calves per cwt.	Lambs per cwt.	All Milk Sold to Plants per cwt.	Broilers per lb.	Turkeys per lb.	Market Eggs per doz.
				---Dollars---					
1990 January	61.70	48.90	75.00	88.00	68.00	12.95	.280	.34	.857
February	64.20	51.70	77.40	87.50	63.80	12.39	.310	.32	.650
March	64.80	52.80	76.50	92.20	68.40	12.17	.340	.35	.804
April	63.90	51.80	78.20	93.00	63.30	11.71	.310	.38	.611
May	66.90	51.90	78.40	91.90	61.10	12.05	.325	.40	.528
June	69.10	51.90	80.50	94.70	58.80	12.19	.320	.41	.589
July	67.00	54.60	75.40	84.50	58.90	12.14	.345	.40	.454
August	66.50	52.90	77.00	87.60	56.30	12.21	.305	.40	.660
September	64.20	50.80	74.00	83.30	57.30	11.78	.320	.36	.701
October	64.40	47.50	74.20	85.80	54.90	11.89	.270	.37	.737
November	64.50	45.60	74.30	86.00	53.30	11.68	.260	.41	.676
December	62.80	47.30	76.70	91.40	51.10	11.15	.265	.41	.778
1990 Average	65.00	50.60	76.40	89.40	60.10	12.02	.305	.38	.675
1989 Average	62.20	46.90	73.70	83.20	69.30	12.37	.345	.38	.632
1988 Average	61.80	46.70	70.40	82.70	70.30	10.94	.340	.35	.427

PRICES RECEIVED FOR VEGETABLE CROPS, CALIFORNIA

Year and Month	Broccoli per cwt.	Cantaloupe per cwt.	Carrots per cwt.	Cauliflower per cwt.	Celery per cwt.	Honeydew Melons per cwt.	Lettuce per cwt.	Market Tomatoes per cwt.
				---Dollars---				
1990 January	14.60	---	11.60	17.20	19.50	---	9.10	---
February	18.10	---	12.70	27.90	10.80	---	6.40	---
March	14.00	---	14.20	21.00	5.95	---	7.30	---
April	13.10	---	9.61	22.10	8.10	---	8.10	---
May	17.30	12.00	7.71	18.80	14.50	26.90	7.85	30.00
June	13.00	11.90	10.20	20.50	8.28	26.90	8.00	23.30
July	22.50	7.00	8.60	21.90	8.25	19.50	12.30	25.10
August	26.10	8.30	8.15	27.90	7.05	11.10	14.50	23.70
September	31.70	7.40	9.25	25.60	9.40	11.00	18.50	23.70
October	37.00	9.20	9.50	33.30	11.50	22.30	18.50	24.40
November	41.70	14.40	16.00	36.20	13.75	37.10	19.80	32.20
December	38.20	---	16.70	32.80	11.50	---	20.90	44.40
							11.00	---
1990 Average	22.30	13.00	11.20	24.80	10.80	15.80	12.20	28.20
1989 Average	20.40	12.60	13.70	27.80	12.90	11.80	11.70	24.00
1988 Average	23.90	15.50	13.00	27.60	11.15	13.10	12.20	29.90

1989-90 AND 1990-91 SEASON RAINFALL, WITH COMPARISONS TO NORMAL

California Stations	1989-90 Precipitation July 1 to June 30	Percent of Normal	1990-91 Precipitation July 1 to June 28	Percent of Normal	Normal Annual Rainfall
	Inches	Percent	Inches	Percent	Inches
NORTH COAST					
Eureka	26.91	70	21.69	56	38.51
Ukiah	22.32	59	23.51	62	38.12
Santa Rosa	19.54	65	21.99	74	29.88
Lakeport	25.95	86	23.44	78	30.04
St. Helena	24.78	70	25.10	71	35.24
CENTRAL COAST					
San Francisco AP	11.87	60	13.43	68	19.71
San Jose	9.52	69	10.88	78	13.86
Livermore	9.66	68	10.59	75	14.11
Salinas AP	8.60	66	9.78	75	13.01
King City	8.38	74	11.54	103	11.25
Paso Robles AP	7.80	62	12.59	100	12.55
SACRAMENTO VALLEY					
Redding	29.15	71	22.74	56	40.95
Willows	10.88	63	16.16	94	17.28
Chico	20.68	80	19.87	77	25.93
Marysville	16.86	82	18.87	92	20.55
Woodland	19.47	109	15.04	84	17.89
Sacramento AP	17.43	102	12.81	75	17.10
SAN JOAQUIN VALLEY					
Stockton AP	10.70	78	9.97	72	13.77
Merced	10.16	84	Missing	Missing	12.05
Fresno AP	10.41	99	9.81	81	10.52
Kettleman Station	4.07	62	8.77	133	6.61
Porterville	7.46	67	10.40	94	11.12
Bakersfield AP	3.72	65	5.74	100	5.72
SOUTH COAST					
Santa Maria AP	6.01	49	14.22	115	12.35
Santa Barbara AP	6.37	39	16.42	101	16.18
Oxnard	4.63	32	12.25	84	14.53
Los Angeles	6.82	56	9.44	78	12.08
Riverside	4.69	49	8.05	84	9.64
San Diego AP	7.84	84	10.94	117	9.32
SOUTHEASTERN INTERIOR					
Bishop AP	2.88	51	4.07	73	5.61
Lancaster	1.60	22	Missing	Missing	7.38
Daggett AP	.45	12	2.56	67	3.81
Thermal AP	.48	17	2.43	86	2.82
Blythe AP	.46	14	2.00	59	3.37
Imperial	Missing	Missing	3.20	133	2.40
CASCADE-SIERRA					
Tulelake	11.90	110	10.00	92	10.84
Alturas	10.67	86	12.58	101	12.45
Mt. Shasta City	28.55	77	Missing	Missing	37.05
Blue Canyon AP	48.13	71	59.64	88	67.87
Yosemite Valley	24.64	68	29.61	82	36.06
Huntington Lake	25.70	69	31.76	85	37.44

SOURCE: National Weather Service Office, Sacramento, CA

ESTIMATED VALUE OF CALIFORNIA'S LEADING AGRICULTURAL EXPORTS VALUED AT PORT OF EXPORTATION CALENDAR YEARS 1989 AND 1990 WITH PERCENTAGE CHANGE

COMMODITY	COMMODITY RANKING		VALUE		VALUE CHANGE	
	1989	1990	1989	1990	1988-89	1989-90
			--- 1,000 Dollars ---		--- Percent ---	
Cotton Lint..................................	1	1	648,453	832,969	— 4	+ 28
Almonds.....................................	2	2	491,874	563,192	— 16	+ 14
Grapes.......................................	3	3	403,321	498,402	+ 5	+ 24
Oranges.....................................	4	4	244,743	252,711	+ 56	+ 3
Beef..	5	5	133,077	130,758	+ 9	— 2
Walnuts......................................	7	6	120,794	130,204	+ 17	+ 8
Prunes.......................................	9	7	101,189	118,398	+ 7	+ 17
Tomatoes....................................	12	8	70,955	96,869	+ 36	+ 37
Wheat..	6	9	128,490	94,831	+ 24	— 26
Alfalfa and Sudan..........................	10	10	83,928	94,137	— 5	+ 12
Lettuce.......................................	16	11	46,889	92,105	+ 4	+ 96
Lemons.......................................	13	12	66,642	83,976	— 28	+ 26
Rice...	8	13	110,506	83,517	— 6	— 24
Strawberries................................	14	14	64,457	74,094	— 17	+ 15
Flowers and Nursery.......................	11	15	72,422	70,087	+ 94	— 3
Peaches......................................	17	16	43,871	69,485	— 18	+ 58
Plums...	18	17	40,657	64,357	— 11	+ 58
Onions..	19	18	38,583	53,759	+ 33	+ 39
Vegetable Seeds...........................	15	19	48,991	53,632	— 21	+ 9
Dairy...	21	20	34,756	43,845	— 52	+ 26
Melons..	24	21	29,999	43,057	— 5	+ 44
Chickens and Eggs.........................	23	22	34,042	40,658	+ 12	+ 19
Broccoli......................................	25	23	29,075	37,473	+ 8	+ 29
Cauliflower...................................	31	24	21,263	35,990	+ 30	+ 69
Safflower.....................................	22	25	34,514	34,793	+ 6	+ 1
Sweet Cherries.............................	20	26	35,437	33,465	— 1	— 6
Asparagus...................................	26	27	28,680	30,715	+ 1	+ 7
Garlic...	33	28	20,043	30,257	+ 70	+ 51
Dry Beans...................................	29	29	24,381	29,527	— 11	+ 21
Celery..	34	30	18,452	29,358	— 18	+ 59
Potatoes.....................................	32	31	20,914	25,372	+ 36	+ 21
Pistachios...................................	28	32	25,369	25,349	+ 66	0
Remaining Estimated Commodities			165,170	147,869		
All Other Commodities			482,949	493,516		
TOTAL....................................			**3,964,886**	**4,538,728**	<1	+ 14

107

California's Agricultural Export Profile, 1990

Commodity	Farm Value of Exports Compared to Total Production Value	CA Export Value Compared To U.S. Export Value at Port of Embarcation	Acres Needed to Produce California Exports (Average Yields)
	Percentage		Acres
Field Crops			
Alfalfa Seed	18.7	23.8	13,311
Hay (incl. alfalfa) Ex. Sudan	3.5	40.1	57,327
Barley	5.9	0.7	11,667
Clover Seed	18.5	61.7	1,519
Cotton Lint	81.3	30.5	858,475
Cottonseed	17.2	18.1	---
Dry Beans	28.7	62.8	48,270
Rice	35.1	15.9	75,291
Safflower	55.0	96.7	64,258
Sudan	89.8	48.4	45,768
Wheat	33.6	2.3	282,004
Fruits and Nuts			
Almonds	70.9	100.0	291,724
Apricots	12.7	82.6	1,888
Avocados	3.6	73.5	2,857
Dates	25.6	100.0	1,364
Figs	15.3	100.0	726
Grapes			
Fresh	21.1	91.0	26,481
Raisins	25.9	100.0	67,434
Processed	4.3	73.4	26,127
Grapefruit	18.8	10.0	2,439
Kiwifruit	30.0	100.0	2,230
Lemons	34.3	85.2	10,473
Olives	1.8	100.0	485
Oranges	25.3	96.3	32,105
Peaches			
Freestone	10.7	78.5	2,969
Clingstone	2.8	100.0	782
Pears	6.6	27.4	1,895
Pistachios	27.3	100.0	16,600
Plums	31.8	86.9	13,336
Prunes	50.8	100.0	42,448
Sweet Cherries	49.4	42.7	4,818
Tangerines	19.6	56.4	1,218
Walnuts	40.3	100.0	71,875
Vegetables			
Asparagus	20.9	77.4	7,449
Broccoli	13.2	96.9	13,844
Carrots	8.7	82.2	4,549
Cauliflower	20.0	96.6	10,574
Celery	11.9	79.7	2,896
Garlic	17.5	100.0	5,456
Lettuce	7.6	80.5	12,766
Melons	8.5	62.9	10,538
Onions	37.5	50.1	14,700
Peppers, Bell	6.3	14.9	1,223
Potatoes	7.6	41.3	3,738
Strawberries	13.3	84.9	1,988
Tomatoes			
Fresh	10.0	30.5	3,580
Processing	3.9	90.5	11,552
Nursery Products			
Flowers and Plants	3.7	35.2	N/A
Vegetable Seeds	N/A	43.8	7,213
Livestock and Poultry			
Beef Cattle and Products	3.0	3.5	---
Dairy Products	2.5	13.7	---
Sheep	3.8	8.9	---
Chickens and Eggs	5.2	5.4	---
Turkeys	0.8	9.9	---
TOTAL, ALL CATEGORIES	---	---	2,192,230